HSG168

FIRE SAFETY
in construction work

Guidance for clients, designers and those

managing and carrying out construction

work involving significant fire risks

HSE BOOKS

First published 1997
Reprinted with amendments 2001

ISBN 0 7176 1332 1

HSG168

This guidance is issued by the Health and
Safety Executive. Following the guidance is
not compulsory and you are free to take
other action. But if you do follow the
guidance you will normally be doing enough
to comply with the law. Health and safety
inspectors seek to secure compliance with
the law and may refer to this guidance as
illustrating good practice.

*Cover photograph shows the fire at
Uppark House which resulted from hot work
carried out by the building contractor. The
photograph was reproduced by kind
permission of the National Trust.*

Contents

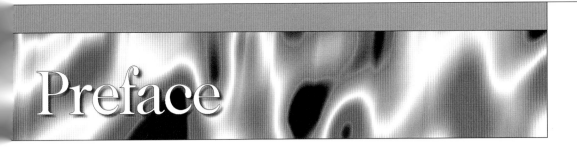

Preface

Every year many construction site workers are killed or injured as a result of their work; others suffer ill health, such as dermatitis, occupational deafness or asbestosis. The hazards are not, however, restricted to those working on sites. Children and other members of the public are also killed or injured because construction activities have not been adequately controlled. The construction industry's performance has improved over the past decade, but the rates of death, serious injury and ill health are still too high.

These deaths, injuries and ill health cause pain and suffering. They also cost money. A recent HSE survey found that accidental loss wasted 8.5% of the tender price, even on a site which had no serious (reportable) accidents.

This book is part of HSE's revised series of health and safety guidance for construction. The series will be developed over the next few years, and will cover approximately 20 key topics. The aim is to help all those involved in construction to identify the main causes of accidents and ill health and explain how to eliminate the hazards and control the risks. The guidance is simple but comprehensive. It will refer to other relevant documents so that you can build up a clear and comprehensive package.

Each piece of guidance will have general relevance to everyone involved in the construction process, from clients to designers, to contractors, individual workers and safety representatives. But some documents will be particularly relevant to specific groups, depending on the subject they address. All the new guidance will be identified with this logo.

Introduction

1   Fire can and does kill or injure wherever it happens. Whenever fire occurs financial loss is incurred. The potential dangers are particularly severe on many construction sites, where risk activities such as hot work are frequently combined with circumstances where fire can spread quickly and escape is difficult. This guidance is about preventing fires starting and ensuring people's safety if they do.

2   The guidance is aimed at construction projects involving substantial fire risks and is relevant to all who have a role in the development, management and application of fire safety standards on construction sites. Construction fire safety needs to be taken into account from early procurement stages right through to final handover. The guidance is therefore relevant to clients, designers and project planners as well as those more directly involved with the management of construction work on site. Whilst the generality of the guidance is applicable to all construction sites, it is to be recognised that specialised projects, such as tunnelling, require particular consideration to satisfactorily address the fire risks, especially to provide adequate general fire precautions. These may necessarily be in excess of those described in this guidance.

3   An information sheet CIS51 *Construction fire safety* has also been produced for those involved in construction projects with lower fire risks such as low-rise housing developments.

4   Not all the safeguards in this guidance will be relevant in all circumstances. What is needed depends on the extent and nature of the risks. This is important since it should not be assumed that small-scale construction work is necessarily low risk. For instance, minor welding repairs undertaken in an oil refinery could have catastrophic consequences if they are not properly controlled. In such cases application of the appropriate safeguards described in this document is vital.

5   This guidance is concerned with the safety of those carrying out construction work. It does not deal with fire-safety requirements for the occupants of completed buildings. However, where construction work takes place in occupied buildings, construction managers need to take account of the implications for occupier staff. This is a matter of liaison with occupiers and the text indicates what issues should be addressed in this respect.

6   The commercial consequences of construction fires can be devastating. There are around 4000 construction fires annually. Approximately 100 of them cause more than £50 000 of damage and usually result in complete dislocation of project schedules. Some, such as the National Westminster Tower (where more than 600 workers were at risk when the fire broke out) and London Underwriting Centre fires, have resulted in losses running into millions.

7   Construction companies and property developers may find it difficult to arrange insurance cover on such potentially high-risk projects unless they can demonstrate good fire safety standards. On larger projects, insurers will normally require compliance at least with *Fire prevention on construction sites. The joint code of practice on the protection from fire of construction sites and buildings undergoing renovation.* This document is produced by the insurance and construction industries. The authors have been consulted during the development of the HSE guidance and there is nothing in this document that conflicts with standards in the joint code.

8   There is a range of legislation which deals with fire safety in construction work. References are given in the *References and further reading* section. In essence, those with control over construction work need to be able to demonstrate that they have:

(a) recognised the risks in their workplaces;

(b) assessed the extent of those risks;

(c) come to an informed decision on the necessary action to combat them;

(d) ensured that the actions decided are implemented.

9   Duty holders may find it easier to incorporate fire into their wider risk management strategies, rather than attempting to deal with fire as a separate issue. In particular, other types of emergency such as security alerts and flooding may involve similar risk management principles, although the detailed requirements to deal with them may differ.

How to use this guidance

10   The guidance is divided into six sections:

- How to stop fire occurring;
- Reducing ignition sources;
- General fire precautions;
- Emergency procedures;
- Temporary accommodation units;
- Sleeping accommodation.

There are a number of appendices to the guidance. Some of them are illustrative. Readers may wish to use the material in them to develop their own management responses to fire risks, but they are not intended to be definitive for all situations. At the back of the book is a reference section, which will help you to find more information.

11   Most significant construction work is covered by the Construction (Design and Management) Regulations 1994 (CDM). Charts in *Appendix 3* describe what each of the CDM duty holders may need to do in respect of each of the six sections. If a client, designer or any other duty holder has a specific question about a specific issue, the charts have been arranged to tell them not only about the issue but also what they should be doing about it.

12   Not all work is covered by the CDM Regulations but even if the specific duties in CDM do not apply, those managing or having control of such work still need to be aware of the material in this guidance and apply it whenever necessary in practice. Even if CDM does not apply, it is based on fundamental principles of good management. There is no reason why managers and the like cannot use similar principles where CDM does not apply.

How to stop fire occurring

13 There are two ways of addressing fire in construction:

(a) prevent it happening in the first place (paragraphs 15–83);

(b) prepare for and deal with the consequences if it does happen (paragraphs 84-161).

Prevention is always better than cure, but both are necessary for construction fire safety.

14 The precautionary measures needed depend on the risks involved. However big the construction project, a risk assessment will always be required. In some cases only simple assessments will be required, but in others much more complicated issues will need to be decided. Ask the question 'if somebody asked us to justify what we've done, could we really do it or would we just be guessing?'

Reducing the amount of combustible material

15 Many materials which can burn have to be used during construction work. The risk of fire decreases as such material is reduced and the smaller any fire will be. There has to be enough material at hand to do the work but this needs to be balanced against the need to reduce the risk of fire. Limit the material present at worksites to what is needed for half a day or a single shift and return unused material to the stores when the work is finished. Where combustible or flammable materials have to be used select the least flammable alternatives.

16 The amount of material kept on site which can burn should be minimised. The need to store such material varies greatly during the life of a site, but try to avoid stockpiling it unless it really is necessary. This can significantly reduce the fire loading and ease congestion on the site.

The changing flammability of materials as they are used

17 Construction work can alter the flammability of substances including nominally flame retardant ones. For instance, when worked on, solid materials (even nominally fire-resisting ones) produce dust, crumbs or other fine material which are always more easily ignited than the bulk material. Remember this when planning construction fire precautions, especially when hot work is used.

General requirements for storage of all combustible materials

18 Ideally, combustible materials need to be stored outside buildings under construction, especially volatile flammable materials such as liquefied petroleum gas (LPG). If combustible materials are stored inside buildings, they need to be kept where, in the case of a fire, the safety of staff is not threatened. For instance, do not put paint stores next to emergency exits.

19 Access to stores should be controlled so that material does not become dispersed haphazardly around the site.

20 If storage outside the structure is not possible, internal stores need to be arranged to limit the spread of fire. Internal stores, especially in more enclosed buildings, may

need to be separated from the rest of the structure by a partition providing at least 30 minutes fire resistance to British Standard BS 476: Part 20, 1987. Good quality plaster-board will usually achieve this and can be very useful for constructing small internal stores. Doors should be fire resisting and self-closing (see paragraph 134).

Storage of more volatile flammable materials

21 Extra precautions are needed with flammable liquids with a flashpoint below 32^0C, eg with many solvents, LPG, flammable gas and oxygen cylinders, especially when stored internally.

22 Good ventilation is needed to prevent dangerous levels of gases accumulating in internal stores. High and low openings in the external wall help to achieve this. The openings should not ventilate into the surrounding structure. Openings representing 1% of the total floor and wall area are sufficient for flammable liquid storage. For flammable gas and oxygen cylinders,

openings representing 2.5% of the total floor and wall area are usually sufficient.

23 Locate external stores in the open air in a well-ventilated area at least 3 metres away from the building's boundaries, drains or excavations (where leaking gas may collect).

24 If this cannot be achieved:
(a) unless the building itself is fire resisting, there should be a fire-resistant partition between the store and the building, located at a distance of 3 metres either side of the store and 9 metres above it;
(b) seal drains and excavations or place a spillage retention wall around the store.

25 External stores should be enclosed by a 1.8 metre high wire-mesh fence for security.

26 Volatile flammable materials may need to be stored inside separate buildings for security reasons. Where buildings are used for this purpose they may not need to be fire resisting if they are in a safe location. They should, however, be of a generally non-combustible construction and be provided with ventilation.

27 Whatever form the storage area takes, unless it is small enough to ensure that no-one

When large amounts of LPG are stored, provide purpose-built, secure accom-modation for it

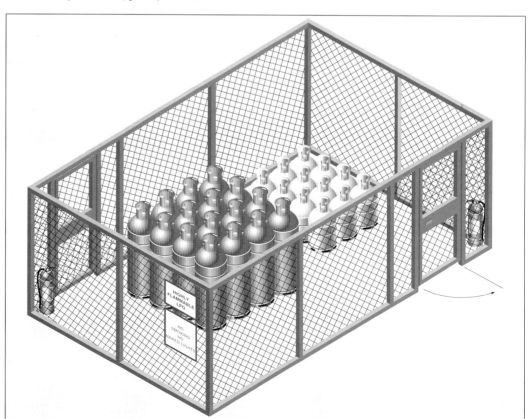

will be trapped in the event of a fire, it should have at least two exits both unlocked when anyone is in it. (A single exit may be adequate when the travel distance does not exceed 12 metres.) Lock the storage area whenever it is unattended.

28 Small quantities of LPG (ie less than 300 kilograms) may be kept in a lockable wire cage with only one exit. Clearly mark the cage and situate it at least 1 metre away from site huts, boundaries, excavations or other features.

29 Small quantities (up to 50 litres) of flammable materials such as paints, solvents and adhesives can be stored in lockable steel chests.

30 Do not store anything other than flammable materials in flammable material stores. Avoid accidental spillage inside the store by banning the decanting of liquids. Flammable liquids, solids and gases should be kept in separate stores.

31 **Never** store LPG in unventilated metal boxes or huts. If there is a leak, gas will build up to a dangerous level.

32 Always store oxygen cylinders separately from cylinders of flammable gases such as LPG and acetylene.

33 For more information on the storage of LPG, read LP Gas Association Code of Practice 7 *Storage of full and empty LPG cylinders and cartridges* and for information on the storage of flammable liquids read HSE guidance note HSG51 *The storage of flammable liquids in containers.*

Rubbish disposal

34 All construction sites, especially in the later stages such as fit-out, can generate large amounts of mostly combustible and easily ignitable rubbish. Implementing simple site rules can prevent the accumulation of rubbish.

The following should be considered:
(a) setting and ensuring that site rules are followed, eg contractors must clear rubbish daily or more often;
(b) providing facilities for storage of rubbish, eg skips;
(c) keeping flammable rubbish, such as contaminated rags, in a closed topped fire-resisting container, eg a metal dustbin;
(d) siting rubbish skips outside and at least 3 metres from the structure and other buildings.

Most construction rubbish can burn. Make sure that it is swept up and removed from the site as soon as possible

35 If a skip is less than 3 metres away from other structures, precautions to prevent skip fires spreading to the structure include:

(a) locating the skip against a fire-resisting wall, eg brick;

(b) using a chute made of non-combustible materials, such as those complying with BS 1703:1977;

(c) restricting the amount of flammable material placed in the skip;

(d) emptying the skip before it contains a significant fire load.

Where sheeted scaffolds form part of the escape route, avoid sheeting the access points so that smoke can escape and the fire brigade can gain access

Some scaffold components have been omitted for clarity

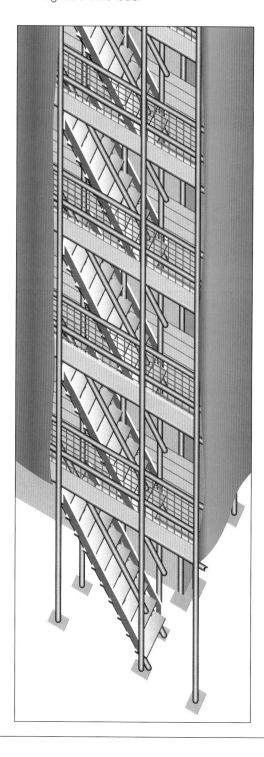

Protective coverings

36 Protective coverings are a common feature during fit-out stages where final fixtures such as doors, handrails, floor coverings and panels need to be protected against damage. Such coverings can be a substantial contribution to the overall fire load in circumstances where ignition sources are common. Particular risks occur where protective coverings are used to protect features in fire escape stairways - this should be avoided. The risk can be reduced by using covering materials that are flame retardant. Those complying with the Loss Prevention Council Standard LPS1207 satisfy flame-retardant criteria. Though they have greater fire-retardant properties, they can still burn and therefore at least one fire escape stairway should be kept free of such protective coverings.

37 Risks arising from protective coverings can be reduced by:

(a) installing vulnerable features needing protection as late as possible in the fit-out stage;

(b) ensuring that the coverings are to flame-retardant specifications wherever possible. This may require liaison with suppliers of vulnerable items and/or protective coverings.

Scaffold sheeting

38 In practice, external scaffolds may prove a valuable escape route in the event of fire, even if they are not specifically intended for this purpose. If scaffolds are sheeted with flammable materials, not only do they contribute to the fire loading, but it would also be unacceptable to rely on them as a significant means of escape. If such reliance is anticipated, scaffold sheeting should be to flame-retardant standards and this is recommended in other circumstances as well. (Sheeting complying with the Loss Prevention Council Standard LPS 1215 satisfies flame-retardant criteria.) If major or sole reliance on escape via a scaffold during fire is anticipated, the need for and extent of

sheeting needs to be carefully considered. Where possible, it should be incomplete in the vicinity of escape ladders and stairs. Not only does this reduce the fire load, it also minimises smoke logging in escape routes and eases fire brigade access.

Handling more volatile flammable substances

39 Flammable liquids, especially highly flammable liquids, need careful handling. Practices to limit the likelihood of spills and the release of flammable vapour concentrations are required; in particular:

(a) provide drip trays to contain spillage during dispensing and decanting;

(b) carry out operations in well-ventilated areas;

(c) use proper handling aids when dispensing from large containers;

(d) keep flammable liquids in secure closed-top containers during conveyance;

(e) do not carry contaminated rags and dispose of them safely.

Further information is given in HSE guidance note HSG140 *The safe use and handling of flammable liquids.*

LPG

40 LPG is widely used across the entire range of construction activities. It is probably the largest single contributor to the risk of fire on construction sites and has been involved in many serious fires and explosions, particularly where there have been leaks in site huts.

Precautions for all uses of LPG

41 The following are important precautions:

(a) Turn off cylinder valves before connecting or disconnecting any equipment. Hoses should never be kinked during disconnection, connection or at any other time. This damages the hose and can easily lead to accidental release of LPG.

(b) Check LPG cylinders and associated fittings before use. If there are any signs of leaking or damage, do not use them. While they may be detected by smell or the hiss of escaping gas, soapy water is a more reliable method of checking for leaks.

(c) During use, secure cylinders in an upright position unless designed to be used in another position, eg on an LPG-fuelled forklift truck. If there is any smell of gas during use, turn off the main cylinder valve immediately and make sure the cause is investigated, determined and put right.

(d) Many appliances will be provided with recommended lighting up instructions and these should be followed. In general, the appliance valve should be closed before the cylinder valve is opened. If the lighting up procedure fails, gas should be allowed to disperse before attempting to relight.

(e) Handle cylinders carefully. Mishandling of cylinders can damage valves and repeated abuse can also lead to serious structural weakness.

42 LPG appliances brought onto site need to be constructed, installed, used and maintained to appropriate standards. For example, there are several relevant British Standards including:

(a) BS EN 521: 1998;

(b) BS EN 1596: 1998;

(c) BS 5482: Part 2,1997;

(d) BS 7261: 1990;

(e) BS 5440: Parts 1 & 2,2000.

When purchasing LPG equipment make sure it complies with these or other equivalent standards.

43 Properly install all appliances and keep them maintained by those who are competent to do so. Ensure that fixed installations are installed by CORGI (Council of Registered Gas Installers) fitters.

44 Adequate ventilation is needed when LPG appliances are used. Where there are fixed installations inside buildings, permanent ventilation openings are required which need to be kept clear.

45 Unless the flame can always be seen by someone in attendance whenever the appliance is used, fit a flame-failure device.

46 Use appliances in accordance with the manufacturer's instructions. Ensure that the instruction booklet is available to the user or that a notice is placed on the appliance.

47 Different appliances are designed to work at different inlet pressures. The correct gas regulator must always be used with the appliance concerned. Check with the manufacturer or a competent gas installer if there is any doubt.

48 Ensure that replacement hoses are of an appropriate standard such as BS 3212: 1991. Use proprietary crimped ends rather than worm drive 'Jubilee' clips. The latter can cause leaks if they are too loose or damage the hose by over-tightening.

Precautions for some particular uses of LPG

49 The following are important precautions during common LPG applications:

Bitumen boilers

(a) LPG cylinders should be kept at least 3 metres from the burner or boiler, or protected by an appropriate heat shield. Where the cylinders are remote they should be sited clear of traffic to prevent damage to the hose (which should be suitably robust; steel reinforced braid, for example).

(b) Never leave boilers unattended while the burner is alight.

(c) Do not tow or move boilers while the burner is alight.

(d) When possible avoid taking tar boilers and similar equipment onto roofs. If this cannot be avoided they should be placed on a non-combustible insulating base to protect the roof from ignition. Equipment should be under the supervision of an experienced operator

Opposite: *In this fire, leaking gas ignited and a man died despite the escape stairway*

and sited where spillages can be easily controlled.

Site huts and similar areas

(a) If equipment leaks or heater flames fail, flammable vapour is able to build up inside site huts and can result in a fire or explosion. It is especially dangerous if vapour accumulates out of hours.

(b) Site huts need to be adequately ventilated at high and low levels and heaters should be properly maintained. Make sure heaters have flame-failure devices incorporated so that the gas supply is shut off if the flame fails.

(c) Where cylinders are an integral part of the appliance (eg cabinet heaters) they may be kept inside the site hut, but where they are separate from the heater keep them outside the hut and

This van fire turned into a major incident when the LPG cylinders started to explode

connected to the heater by the shortest practicable length of suitable hose or piping.

(d) In both cases the fuel supply must be turned off at the appliance and the cylinder after use (and especially when the site closes overnight or at weekends). Always keep heaters clear of obstruction, eg clothing.

Transport of LPG

50 Use open vehicles to transport cylinders upright. Ideally LPG should not be carried on vehicles with other flammable materials, eg paints, solvents, etc. If this is unavoidable, the other materials should be kept in a closed steel chest or box and well away from the cylinders. Two dry powder extinguishers should be carried, nominally 2 and 6 kilogram.

51 Drivers carrying more than two cylinders of LPG need to have received instruction and, if necessary, training about LPG hazards and what they have to do in an emergency. The driver should also carry in the cab a Transport Emergency Card ('Tremcard') containing details of the load carried and appropriate emergency action. The purpose of this is to provide the emergency services with reliable information on the problem they are faced with as soon as they arrive on the scene.

Demolition

52 Demolition work can involve a high risk of fire and explosion. In particular:

(a) dismantling of tank structures causing ignition of flammable residues;

(b) disruption and ignition of buried gas services.

53 Buried and other service pipes should always be assumed to be present on a site unless it is positively confirmed that they are not. Identify the location of gas services before any demolition work begins. The client or local supply company will often be able to provide indications of where pipes and cables are located, but this should always be accompanied by a survey of the site. A competent person should do the survey using services' locating devices. Once the location of all services is identified, make arrangements to ensure that they are disconnected from the mains supply by a competent person and purged of any residual gas. It is extremely dangerous to merely assume that this has been done. It needs to be confirmed by a formal process in which a competent person, usually a representative of the local supply company, gives authoritative assurance of disconnection and clearance.

54 Even if removal of the services is not an intended part of the demolition job, it is still important to locate and isolate services to

avoid damaging them. In some cases it may be necessary for supply systems to remain charged. In such cases particular care will be needed in implementing systems of work to minimise the risk of contact.

55 Storage tanks often contain residues of flammable materials which can result in flammable and explosive concentrations. This is especially dangerous when hot work dismantling methods are used before the tank has been thoroughly cleaned. This work is potentially extremely dangerous and those doing it must have the specialised competence to do it safely.

56 A full description of the extensive precautions needed in this work is beyond the scope of this guidance. Further information is contained in HSE guidance note CS15 *The cleaning and gas freeing of tanks containing flammable residues.* Primary measures include:

(a) clearly identifying the contents of tanks and associated pipework;

(b) cleaning tanks and pipework before dismantling work begins;

(c) keeping to clearly defined systems of work during dismantling (permit-to-work (PTW) systems will be appropriate, see paragraphs 68-72);

(d) avoiding hot work wherever possible, for example, by the use of hydraulically powered shears.

Reducing ignition sources

Smoking

57 Discourage smoking on all sites and in higher risk situations control or ban it altogether, for instance, in any areas where highly flammable materials such as some cellular foam plastics, highly flammable liquids and gas cylinders are stored or used.

58 Bring the smoking rules to the attention of all workers and visitors to the site. Display the appropriate signs, particularly in high-risk or communal areas such as canteens and site access points.

59 Consider the need for designated safe areas where smoking is allowed and provide tin ashtrays filled with sand in these areas.

60 Check that people keep to the smoking rules and enforce them positively.

Plant and equipment

61 Select plant, both electrical and engine driven, to match the demands placed upon it to prevent overheating during use; especially in dusty conditions.

62 Maintain all plant properly and in particular air filters and intakes should be regularly cleaned in dusty conditions. Ensure that air intakes are positioned so that air is free from flammable gases and vapours.

63 Refuelling (especially with petrol) should take place in the open air or in well-ventilated spaces away from ignition sources. Bulk storage tanks should be bunded.

64 Ideally, securely fasten lamps to a solid backing. If they are mounted on tripods make sure that the tripod cannot be dislodged or overturned. Make sure that electrical equipment is not inadvertently covered and that due care is taken in positioning, especially halogen

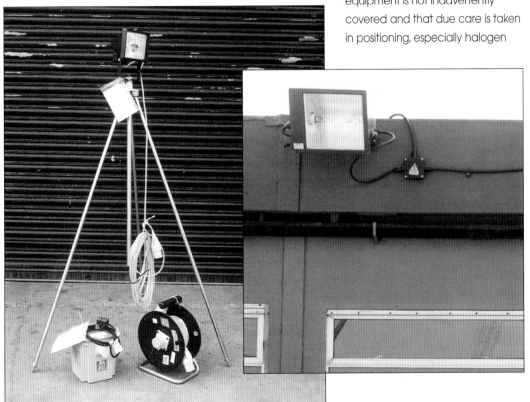

Left: **a lamp attached to a tripod**

Right: **a lamp bolted to a solid backing**

lamps and heaters, to ensure that they cannot ignite any combustible material nearby.

65 Protect plant and equipment when used in areas where a potentially flammable atmosphere may occur, such as in LPG, highly flammable liquids (HFLs) storage areas, paint spraying or floor laying with HFLs. Only use electrical equipment that is certified as constructed to a suitable British Standard or an equivalent explosion protection standard. Equipment which is not explosion protected should be kept a safe distance away, usually 4 metres, from any areas where there is a risk of explosion. More detailed advice on zoning is contained in BS 5345: Part 2, 1989 and HSE guidance note HSG140 *The safe use and handling of flammable liquids.*

Use of oxy-fuel equipment

66 Workers should be competent in the use of such work practices.

67 Provision and maintenance of the correct equipment are key factors in preventing incidents. Detailed guidance is given in HSE guidance note HSG139 *The safe use of compressed gases in welding, flame cutting and allied processes,* and in the British Compressed Gases Association Code of Practice No 7 but the following precautions address more common problems.

(a) Regulators and hoses should be of a recognised standard, eg BS EN ISO 2503: 1998 and BS EN 559: 1994.

Typical equipment used in gas welding and allied processes. Note (a) flashback arresters and (b) non-return valves

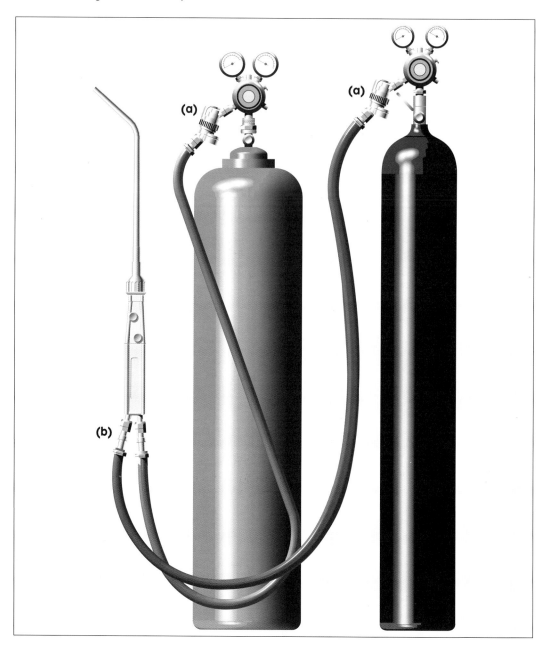

(b) To avoid confusion hoses should be colour coded as follows:

- blue - oxygen;
- red - acetylene;
- orange - propane.

(c) Non-return valves at the torch/blowpipe inlet on both gas lines are strongly recommended, as is a flame arrester with a cut-off valve, sometimes known as a '**flashback arrester**', at the pressure regulator outlet from acetylene gas cylinders. Indeed it is considered good safe working practice and is highly advisable to similarly fit a '**flashback arrester**' at the pressure regulator outlet from other fuel gas and oxygen cylinders, too. All such safety devices should be to an appropriate standard, such as BS EN 730: 1995.

(d) Use proprietary hose assemblies with hose connectors crimped to hose ends. Worm drive fasteners ('Jubilee clips') are not recommended. They may be the wrong size and over-tightening them can damage the hose.

(e) Make sure that oil or grease does not contaminate the oxygen supply. Only use components which have been specially cleaned and supplied for oxygen use.

(f) Always check equipment visually for damage before use, especially the hoses. When you have assembled the equipment always check for leaks by applying a soap solution around joints and watching for bubbles.

(g) Gas cylinders should be secured in a vertical position. Hose length should be kept to a minimum. This reduces the likelihood of damage and should help to ensure that the hose is not damaged by the hot work.

Permit to work (PTW) systems

68 All hot work generating heat, sparks or flame can cause a fire. To avoid this, PTW systems should be considered. Where hot work is not often carried out and where the risk of fire is low, there is less need for formal systems of management control. However, as the amount of hot work and the risks associated with it increase, the need for formal PTW systems increases. They are particularly useful where there are numerous hot work operations taking place and where there is a lot of com-bustible material present, both incidentally and as part of the building structure.

69 PTWs are formal management documents. They should only be issued by those with clearly assigned authority to do so and the requirements stated in them must be complied with before the permit is issued and the work covered by it is undertaken. Individual PTWs should relate to clearly defined individual pieces of work. Do not use PTW documents as blanket authorisations to carry out hot work anywhere on the site at any time. (More general standards for site-wide hot work can be set out in site rules.)

70 PTWs should normally include:
(a) the location and nature of the hot work intended;
(b) the proposed time and duration of the work;
(c) the limits of time for which the permit is valid;
(d) the person in direct control of the work.

71 Precautions to be taken and reflected in the PTW before, during and after the work include:
(a) clearing the surrounding area of all loose combustible material;
(b) where work takes place on one side of a wall or partition the other side should be checked for combustible material;
(c) having suitable extinguishers at hand and a careful watch maintained for fire during the work, and following completion after it;
(d) protecting combustible material which cannot be cleared;
(e) examining the hot work area thoroughly for some time after the work has finished. (Typically this will be at least an hour but ignition can sometimes occur much later than this. Inform the night security guards where hot work has been going on and ask them to check these areas);
(f) in view of the potential risk it is a sensible precaution for all hot work to

stop by a safe period before the end of the day.

72 You may not need a fully documented PTW system where the risks arising from hot work are low; however, precautions such as having a fire extinguisher are still required. Site rules are an effective means of making these precautions clear to those carrying out such work.

Electrical installations

73 Electrical installations, especially temporary ones, should be of sufficient capacity for the intended use and designed, installed, inspected and maintained by competent personnel. The installation should meet BS 7671: 1992 requirements for electrical installations, which includes a special section on construction sites. Do not allow ad hoc additions or alterations to the electrical installation by personnel who are not competent. Electrical equipment should meet standards that reflect the adverse conditions on most construction sites such as:

(a) BS EN 60309-1: 1999;

(b) BS 7375: 1996;

(c) BS EN 60439-4: 1991;

(d) BS 4363: 1991.

74 Some common electrical faults posing fire risks include:

(a) use of flat twin and earth cable as extension leads instead of suitable flexible cable;

(b) overloading of sockets in site accommodation;

(c) cable laid in or near combustible material, frequently in roof and ceiling voids. Accumulation of rubbish against distribution boards poses similar fire risks and often occurs when installations are located in quiet parts of the site;

(d) intentional defeating of safety devices, such as fuses or circuit breakers;

(e) mechanical damage to cables, often as a result of inappropriate routing of cables;

(f) make-shift cable joints made without correct proprietary connectors.

75 The proper use of electrical safety devices such as residual current devices (RCDs) can reduce the risks of fire arising from electrical faults. However, they do not substitute for properly designed, installed, inspected and maintained electrical installations under the supervision of an electrically competent person.

76 In order to design and install a system which is safe with adequate capacity, those responsible need to be informed about its likely use. Electrical systems need to be periodically checked to ensure that they remain safe and free from damage or deterioration. They should also be checked before any addition, extension or modification is carried out. On most sites, and particularly larger ones, this will require some form of systematic electrical inspection and maintenance regime.

Bonfires

77 For safety reasons (and sometimes environmental protection), bonfires should not normally be allowed on construction sites. There should be alternative arrangements for the proper disposal of rubbish and other waste materials.

78 If, under exceptional circumstances, a bonfire is needed the following precautions apply.

(a) Only light fires on an open site on designated ground and far enough removed (typically 10 metres) so that there is no risk of setting adjoining material, storage areas or structures alight.

(b) Large open bonfires can easily get out of control. Limit the amount burnt in one go to what can be dealt with in an incinerator, eg a 50 gallon oil drum which has been properly cleaned of flammable residues and provided with ventilation holes.

(c) Never leave fires unattended until they are completely out, damping down if necessary.

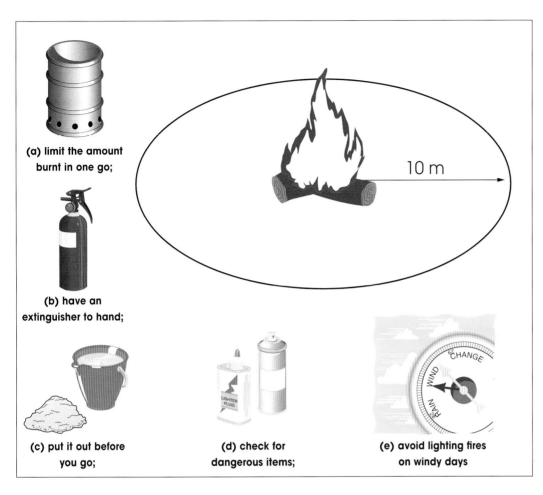

(a) limit the amount burnt in one go;

(b) have an extinguisher to hand;

10 m

(c) put it out before you go;

(d) check for dangerous items;

(e) avoid lighting fires on windy days

Avoid lighting bonfires unless you really need to. If you do, make sure you follow points (a) to (e)

(d) Attendants should have the correct fire extinguishers or other suitable equipment to hand.

(e) Material should be checked for dangerous items such as empty cylinders, aerosol cans and flammable substances, before it is brought to the fire.

(f) Do not light fires on windy days.

(g) Do not site bonfires where flames, smoke and any airborne debris might affect overhead electrical lines.

79 Petrol or other similar accelerants should **never** be used to start or fuel any fire on any construction site. Instead, use paper or similar kindling to start bonfires.

Arson and site security

80 Arson is a real and substantial risk on all sites, particularly where there are trespassers. Measures should be in place to prevent unauthorised access, especially of children. Care is needed to ensure that no gaps develop in the fencing/hoarding around the site.

81 Securely store (or if necessary remove) flammable liquids, LPG and other combustible materials while the site is closed.

82 Some sites may be particularly vulnerable to arson, especially those with a high fire loading or in localities with a known history of vandalism and arson, or where protective hoarding is not possible. In such cases additional security measures beyond a perimeter fence should be considered, for instance:

(a) regular out-of-hours security patrols or a permanent security presence;

(b) security lighting;

(c) liaison with the local police force;

(d) closed circuit television monitoring.

Security staff need to be alert to the possibility of detecting fire and know what to do if they discover it.

83 Arson is sometimes thought to be committed by site employees, eg unexplained skip fires. Site managers and site security staff should be aware of this potential and the need to be alert for signs of it during their inspections.

General fire precautions

3

84 If there is a fire, people need to be able to evacuate the structure and possibly the construction site itself, to reach a place of safety. **It cannot be overemphasised that the main aim is to ensure everyone reaches safety if there is a fire.** Putting it out is secondary to this. The term general fire precaution (GFP) is used to describe the structural features and equipment needed to achieve this aim. It covers:

(a) escape routes and fire exits;

(b) fire-fighting equipment;

(c) raising the alarm;

(d) making emergency plans;

(e) limiting the spread of fire (compartmentation).

85 The GFPs needed will vary from site to site. Sometimes they will be very simple and other times much more complicated depending on the risks involved, but they all need to take account of the size of the site, the number of people present and the nature of the work being done.

86 The purpose of this section is to help decide which GFPs are appropriate in particular construction circumstances. An essential requirement is that GFPs and people's ability to escape should not depend on ad hoc arrangements, such as the use of manipulative devices, eg portable or throw-out ladders, or rely on rescue by others, such as the fire brigade.

Means of escape

87 Escape routes need to be available for everyone on the site. On open-air sites and unenclosed single-storey structures, such routes may be both obvious and plentiful. However, in more complicated structures,

especially where work is above or below ground, more detailed consideration will be needed.

(a) Proper provision is needed for all workers, wherever they are and however transient the activity, eg workers on the roof or in a plant or lift gear room.

(b) During the course of construction, escape routes are likely to change and possibly become unavailable. It is important that replacement routes are provided and identified early.

(c) Building designs often incorporate fire escape routes for the eventual

This means of escape has been blocked off and will be useless in the confusion of a fire

occupiers. For new buildings these should be installed at the earliest stage possible. For buildings being refurbished, try and arrange the work to make use of existing escape routes and keep them available.

(d) In an emergency, escape via a scaffold is difficult. Try to minimise reliance on it. Where possible, provide well-separated alternative access from a scaffold to escape routes in the main building floor. (If this is not possible see paragraph 104).

(e) There should normally be at least two escape routes in different directions.

88 Escape routes need to be clear uncomplicated passageways, properly maintained and kept free of obstruction.

89 A basic principle of escape routes is that any person confronted by an outbreak of fire, or the effects from it, can turn away from it or pass it safely to reach a place of safety.

90 Where this cannot be realistically accommodated, it is important to ensure that the risk of being trapped by a fire in dead-end situations is minimised. The risk can be reduced by ensuring that anybody in a dead-end does not have to pass through an area

of higher fire hazard to reach a place of safety, and keeping the distance they have to travel in the dead-end as short as possible. For example:

(a) where operations of high fire risk are carried out, such as laying floor coverings or work on pipes which have carried flammable materials, nobody should have to negotiate their way past the work area or plant to make their escape;

(b) combustible materials should not be stored or allowed to accrue at the exits from dead-ends, such as by doorways from rooms; or along the escape routes from dead-ends which are narrow or restricted, such as along corridors.

Travel distance

91 In a fire the effects of smoke and heat can spread quickly. It is important not to over-estimate how far people can travel before they are adversely affected by fire. Appropriate distances to reach safety will depend on a variety of matters including how quickly the fire grows, the structure and layout of the building, the location of the fire and where people are relative to this.

Avoid creating dead-ends

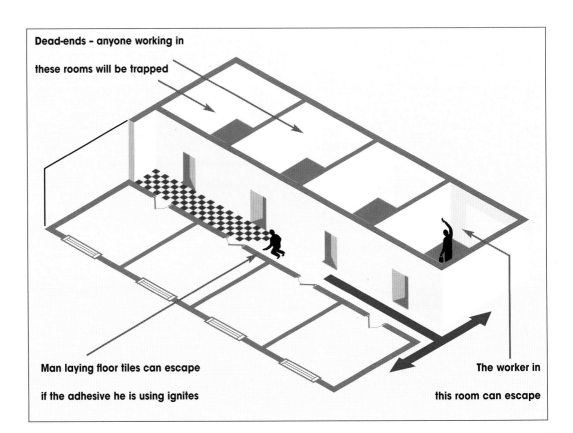

Dead-ends - anyone working in these rooms will be trapped

Man laying floor tiles can escape if the adhesive he is using ignites

The worker in this room can escape

Table 1: Travel distances

| | Fire hazard | | |
	Low	*Normal*	*High*
Enclosed structures:			
alternative	60 metres	45 metres	25 metres
dead-end	18 metres	18 metres	12 metres
Semi-open structures:			
alternative	200 metres	100 metres	60 metres
dead-end	25 metres	18 metres	12 metres

Notes

Semi-open structures are completed or partially constructed structures in which there are substantial openings in the roof or external walls, which would allow smoke and heat from any fire to readily disperse.

Alternative escape routes should, where possible, proceed in substantially opposite directions. The principle is that they are sufficiently apart that any fire should not immediately affect both routes. As such they should not be less than 45^0 apart.

Dead-end travel distances are significantly restricted. This is so people have time to negotiate their way past any fire between them and the exit, before it threatens their escape.

Low hazard areas are those where there is very little flammable or combustible material present and the likelihood of fire occurring is low. Examples could be steel or concrete clad framework or structures in pre-fitting-out stages.

Normal hazard areas will cover the majority of situations. Flammable and combustible materials are present, but of such a type and disposition that any fire will initially be localised.

High hazard areas are locations where significant quantities of flammable or combustible materials are present of such a type that in the event of a fire rapid spread will occur, possibly accompanied by evolution of copious amounts of smoke or fume. As such, normal precautions discussed previously to minimise the fire load, should ensure that such areas are rare on construction sites. Examples of where they might occur are demolition or refurbishment work involving oil-contaminated wooden floors or linings, and fixing floor and wall coverings using flammable adhesives.

92 Table 1 gives maximum travel distances which experience has shown can be considered acceptable for a variety of situations. The distances given are from the fire to an exit from the structure, typically a door, leading to the outside at ground level; or to a stairway or compartment protected against fire (see *Stairways*, paragraphs 94 and *Compartmentation*, paragraph 134).

93 The travel distances are measured as the person walks and not as the crow flies. Care should be taken to minimise obstructions so that maximum travel distances are not exceeded. It is sensible to arrange the work to keep travel distances as short as possible.

Stairways

94 Careful consideration needs to be given to the means of escape from work areas above or below ground level. It is especially important to ensure that the stairways and ladders are located or protected such that any fire will not prevent people using them.

95 Except for small two-storey buildings with travel distances well within those given in Table 1 for dead-end travel, there is normally a need for at least one stairway to be protected against any fire in the main work area affecting it. In the finished building this is typically provided by siting the stairway in its own dedicated fire-resisting shaft. In these circumstances the travel distance is measured from the worksite to the door of the protected stairway.

96 Protected stairways will be a feature in many buildings. It is therefore a sensible precaution to install these and make them available as early as is practicable in the construction of new structures, before fire risks increase such as when fitting-out starts.

97 Ceiling, wall or floor coverings which if ignited would allow the fire to spread rapidly, or the effects from it to be exacerbated, should not be used in escape stairways. The ideal surfaces are plaster or concrete, which may be painted or sealed as appropriate. Protective coverings in escape stairways should be flame retardant (see paragraph 36).

98 Where possible it is sensible to try and provide alternative protected stairways. For structures which are more than four storeys above ground this is considered essential. With the exception of small basements, on subterranean structures, at least one stairway should exit to the open air at ground level.

Doors

99 Doors giving access to protected stairways need to be fire resistant and fitted with effective proprietary self-closing devices. The nominal minimum period of fire resistance

considered appropriate for protected stairways is 0.5 hour, which the doors should be designed to meet. An appropriate constructional standard for doors to comply with is BS 476: Part 22,1987, and for their installation BS 8214: 1990

100 The doors leading to the protected stairway and the final exit from it should open outwards in the direction that people will escape. Revolving doors are not considered suitable as they can jam. For similar reasons avoid sliding doors.

101 The doors must be openable from the escape side. If security is required, proprietary fastenings should be used, such as those which comply with BS EN 1125: 1997 or other relevant standard. Opening a door should not depend on using a key.

102 The integrity of the enclosure containing the stairway is critical to its safe use in an emergency. Check that the doors are properly maintained and close correctly. It is also important to check that there are no other openings present or made, eg for pipes, wiring and ductwork. If there are, they need to be in-filled at the earliest opportunity. In refurbishment work, do not assume that there

(a) Fire doors need to be kept closed and clearly marked when they form part of the escape route

(b) This escape route will quickly fill with smoke in a fire because no fire door is fitted

are no holes breaching the enclosure of protected stairways in the existing structure. Fire can also spread rapidly over false ceilings.

External escape stairs and ladders

103 If the nature of the work means it is not reasonable to provide or maintain an internal protected stairway, external temporary escape stairs may be provided instead. Adequate stairways can be constructed from scaffolding; you can use wooden treads and platforms. The important requirement is that the external wall against which the stairway is erected should be imperforate and afford a nominal period of 0.5 hour fire resistance for 9 metres vertically below the stairway and 1.8 metres either side and above, as

measured from the stair treads. This means that all doors, apart from the uppermost one leading on to the external stairway should have 0.5 hour fire resistance and be self-closing. Any other openings, including windows which are not of fire-resisting construction, should be suitably protected, eg with plaster-board, proprietary mineral fibre reinforced cement panels or steel sheets.

104 In the open air, such as work on the initial framework of a structure, it is unlikely that an imperforate barrier will be available to separate the escape stairway from the work area. In such circumstances, unless the travel distances are well within those given in Table 1 for dead-end travel, at least two alternative routes should be provided. These should be

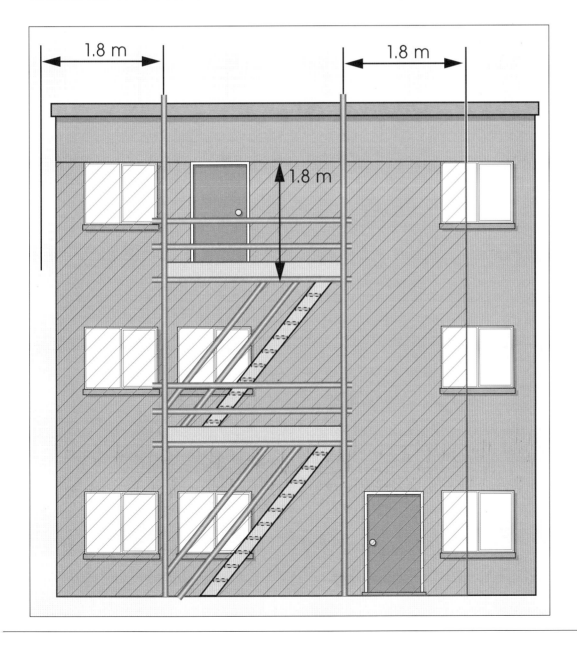

Temporary scaffold based escape routes need to be protected from fire inside the building. The windows inside the shaded area need to be blocked off with fire-resisting material. The platform has to be sufficiently wide to allow the door to open fully and give safe access to the stairway.

Some scaffold components have been omitted for clarity

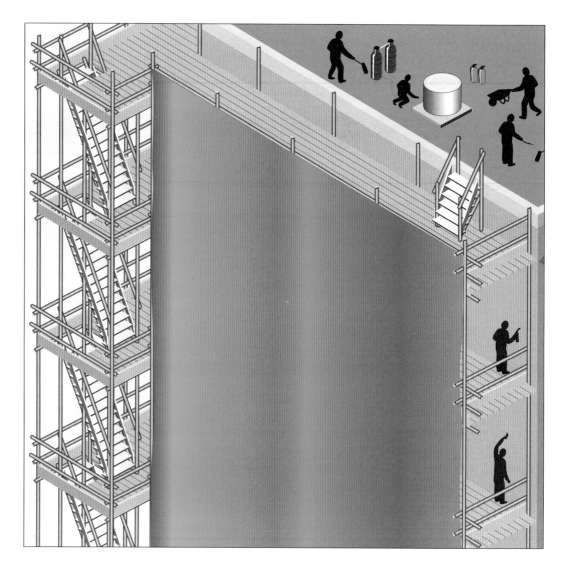

In this job, hot work on the roof and window renovation using blowlamps and substantial amounts of flammable substances mean the fire risk is high. Escape via ladders inside the sheeting could be difficult so external access is provided at one end

Some scaffold components have been omitted for clarity, eg roof edge protection is required

well apart, ideally at opposite ends. If the structure or building is within a sheeted enclosure, eg for weather protection, environmental or safety reasons, at least one of the routes should be outside the enclosure.

105 The escape route should lead away from the enclosure where possible.

Escape route sizing

106 While stairways, etc, may be adequate for normal entry and exit, it is important not to overestimate their capacity in an emergency, when bottlenecks can easily occur. Recommended widths are related to the number of people expected to use them in an emergency. For example, a stairway (in a building under construction) serving two floors should normally be a minimum of 1000 millimetres wide to adequately cater for about 200 people. However, if the door leading to or

from this is only 750 millimetres wide, the escape route via this door is only considered adequate for about 100 people.

107 More detailed advice on the size of escape routes can be found in the BS 5588 (Parts 0-11) series of standards, and in Approved Document B and the Technical Standards which support the Building Regulations and Building Standard (Scotland) Regulations respectively. The majority of structures will be built in compliance with one of these. Therefore, in most cases the early installation of these escape routes will provide adequate means of escape during construction work. However, if during the construction work the number of people present is greater than the design maximum of the finished building, additional escape routes, or increased sizing of these might well be necessary.

108 While not ideal, ladders under certain circumstances, such as limited space, may be used instead of stairs. However, the speed at which people can escape via ladders is much slower. In emergencies, the number using a vertical ladder, with stagger every 6 metres is considered to be 10 able-bodied persons. For a ladder, with a maximum rake of 60^0 to the horizontal and 6 metres length between platforms, 30 able-bodied people.

Assembly points

109 All designated escape exits from the structure should give direct access to an unenclosed space in the open air at ground level. From here, there should be an unobstructed passageway from the structure to a place of safety where people can assemble and be accounted for. Regard needs to be given to the size and location of these assembly points:

(a) on small sites, the pavement outside may be adequate;

(b) on larger sites, arrangements may have to be made to make use of an area such as a car park;

(c) on sites such as chemical refineries, a safe refuge such as a plant control room might have to be used.

110 Where the construction site is surrounded by a hoarding or fence, and the assembly point is outside this, an adequate number of gates giving access to the assembly point will be needed. There should be clear and unobstructed access to the gates, which should be unlocked and available for use at all times people are at work on the site.

Emergency signs

111 Escape routes need to be clearly indicated by proper signs. The Health and Safety (Safety Signs and Signals) Regulations 1996 set the standards for these signs. They should comprise a white pictogram on a green background; supplemented with text if appropriate. Signs which comply with

BS 5499: Part 1,1990 (amended 1993) will meet the requirements of the Regulations. See HSE guidance L64 *Safety signs and signals: Guidance on regulations* for further details.

112 Signs need to be large enough so that they can be clearly seen and positioned where they are least likely to be obstructed or obscured by smoke. Typically this is about 2 metres above the floor, but the layout of the site may make alternative positioning more appropriate.

113 If emergency lighting is required (see *Emergency lighting*, paragraph 137) it may be convenient to use units which incorporate the appropriate fire safety sign. Signs containing photo-luminescent materials can also emphasise escape routes where lighting is poor.

Emergency signs

114 Supplementary signs may also be required to clarify escape procedures. For example, to inform how to open the door if this is not obvious, or where a patent security device is fitted, such as a 'Push bar to open' sign. Similarly where there is danger that a fire exit may become obstructed, a conspicuous 'Keep clear - Fire escape' sign should be displayed. Signs complying with BS 5499: Part 1,1990 (amended 1993) are acceptable.

115 Signs need to be sufficiently durable to withstand site conditions, securely fastened and properly maintained (including kept clean).

116 If circumstances alter and any sign becomes inappropriate, it should be removed. For example, if an escape route is changed it is imperative that signs giving misleading or confusing information are taken down.

A temporary, wired-in fire alarm during major renovation of a large and complex multi-storey building

Fire alarms

117 The aim of any fire warning system is to ensure that people on the site are alerted to make their escape well before a fire becomes life-threatening. The essential requirements of the fire warning signal are that it is distinctive, clearly audible above any other noise and is recognised by all the people on site.

118 The sophistication of the method of giving warning of fire will vary from site to site. For example:

(a) on small open-air sites, or those involving small buildings and structures, 'word of mouth' may well be adequate;

(b) on larger open-air sites, or those involving buildings and structures with a limited number of rooms, such that a shout of 'fire' might not be heard or could be misunderstood, a klaxon, whistle, gong or small self-contained proprietary fire alarm unit may well be needed;

(c) on sites for complex multi-storey buildings, it is likely that a wired-in system of call-points and sounders will be required to provide an effective fire warning system. For example, one that meets the requirements of BS 5839: Part 1,1988.

119 Fire alarm systems will often be fitted as part of the construction work. Alternatively, buildings may have a wired-in fire warning system already installed. Try and plan the work to install the fire warning system as early as possible, and where a system is already installed, keep it in working order for as long as possible. Where they are relied on during the construction phase, it is vital that existing systems are not inadvertently disabled, for instance during work on electrical systems in refurbishment work. If they are disabled, for any reason, alternative arrangements need to be provided.

120 There is not normally any need for automatic fire detectors to be fitted during construction work. However, if there are locations where a fire might occur and develop unnoticed until it threatens people's means of escape, detectors may be appropriate. Domestic type smoke detectors are not considered appropriate on complex multi-storey sites. However, they may be suitable for use on smaller sites, where despite their comparatively low volume, they could still be effective.

121 Indicator panels sometimes form part of more sophisticated alarm systems. They

can provide information on the location of the fire, though this may prove erroneous if a call-point is activated elsewhere than in the vicinity of the fire. However, providing people are aware of the constraints of the system and understand what the signals mean, they can help inform what emergency actions have been taken, and be of use to the attending fire brigade.

122 When a fire is detected and the alarm raised, all should make their escape without delay. If it is possible that a false alarm could cause significant problems, procedures to verify the outbreak of a fire should be developed. For example, on raising the alarm, perhaps by activation of a call-point, an intercom system might be provided adjacent to this to allow verbal confirmation. This could be to a control centre from which the main alarm is then raised. Alternatively, the person in the control centre might be in radio contact with somebody on the fire floor. Safeguards need to be built into such procedures to ensure that while anyone is on site the control centre is **always** occupied (including during breaks), and if the system for verbal communication fails, effective sounding of the alarm is not delayed.

123 The operation and effectiveness of the fire warning system over the entire site should be:
(a) routinely checked and tested by a responsible person;
(b) periodically serviced and any necessary rectification or repair carried out by a competent person having the appropriate level of training and experience.
The work should be carried out in accordance with the supplier's instructions, or where relevant, to an appropriate standard, for example BS 5839: Part 1, 1988. Keep records of the work carried out. It is particularly important to check the effective operation in practice of the alarm systems that rely on verbal communications described in paragraph 122.

124 It is especially important to ensure that as the site develops the alarm system is modified so that effective coverage of the entire site is maintained.

125 General means for communication should be tested daily, eg portable radios should be checked at the start of shifts. Servicing should be in accordance with supplier recommendations.

Fire-fighting equipment

126 As well as providing fire extinguishers for specific activities, such as hot work or LPG storage, they should also be located at identified fire-points around the site. Unless the equipment itself is predominantly red in colour and the location self-evident, identification of the fire-point is probably best achieved by providing a stand which is substantially red in colour, or providing an appropriate safety sign (ie, one which complies with the Health and Safety (Safety Signs and Signals) Regulations 1996 or BS 5499: Part 1, 1990 (amended 1993)).

127 The primary purpose of fire extinguishers is to tackle incipient fires to **enable people to make their escape**. Putting out larger fires is the fire services' role. The extinguishers should be appropriate to the nature of the potential fire:
(a) wood, paper and cloth - water, foam or multi-purpose dry powder extinguisher;
(b) flammable liquids - dry powder or foam extinguisher;
(c) electrical - carbon dioxide (CO_2) or dry powder extinguisher.

128 Extinguishers should conform to a recognised standard, such as BS 5423:1987 or BS EN 3: 1996. It is also important that there is an appropriate scheme to ensure they are regularly checked and properly maintained. This is not only to ensure that they are available and ready for use, but that accidents do not occur to the person using them, as the containers are pressurised.

129 Examine fire extinguishers and hose reels at least annually in accordance with a recognised procedure, such as that detailed in BS 5306: Part 3, 2000 and BS 5306: Part 1,

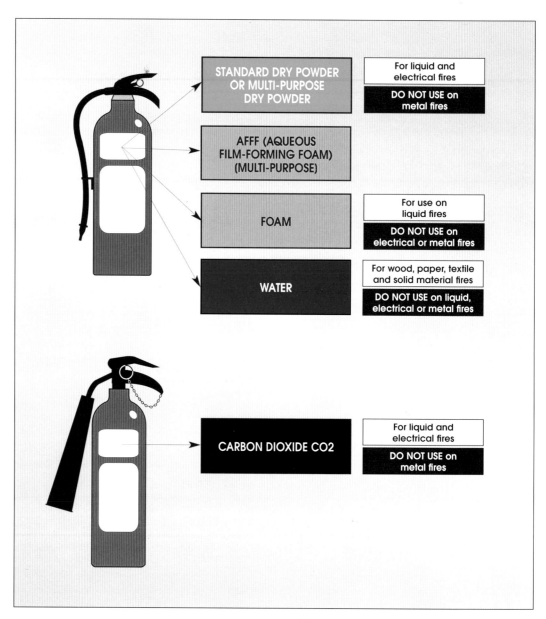

A selection of fire extinguishers

Fire extinguishers complying with BS EN 3: 1996 are red with a coloured zone identifying the extinguishing agent (eg blue for dry powder)

STANDARD DRY POWDER OR MULTI-PURPOSE DRY POWDER	For liquid and electrical fires / DO NOT USE on metal fires
AFFF (AQUEOUS FILM-FORMING FOAM) (MULTI-PURPOSE)	
FOAM	For use on liquid fires / DO NOT USE on electrical or metal fires
WATER	For wood, paper, textile and solid material fires / DO NOT USE on liquid, electrical or metal fires
CARBON DIOXIDE CO2	For liquid and electrical fires / DO NOT USE on metal fires

1976 respectively. The work should be carried out by a competent person who has received appropriate training. The date and results of the examinations should be recorded, often on a service sticker attached to the individual piece of equipment, so that the particular extinguisher or hose reel checked is identifiable.

130 The number and type of extinguishers present, depends on the fire hazard. For a typical spread of fire hazards, the following is considered to provide a reasonable level of cover:

(a) one 9 litre water or foam; and
(b) one CO_2 extinguisher (at least 1.1 kilograms)

per 200 m^2 of floor area with not less than two each of (a) and (b) on each floor.

Note: Dry powder extinguishers (at least 9 kilograms) may be provided in addition to or substituted for any of these extinguishers, especially where the nature of the fire hazard warrants this.

131 Hose reels may also be used instead of the water-based extinguishers. One per 800 m^2 of floor area is recommended, but make sure it can reach all points of the area to be covered. Hose reels should be of an appropriate standard, such as BS 5306: Part 1, 1976, and as with extinguishers they need to be regularly checked and properly maintained.

132 It is important that everyone knows how to use the fire-fighting equipment. All fire-fighting equipment should have clear operating instructions with it. Those carrying out higher risk activities, such as hot work, need to

Plasterboard partitions such as this can form effective compartmentation. It is important that all gaps are filled in. In this case there are holes in the top of the partition and service ducts in the side rooms that need to be sealed

be completely competent in the use of the fire-fighting equipment provided and training will normally be required to achieve this.

133 Larger and more complex structures, such as multi-storey buildings, may have fixed fire-fighting systems installed. These may range from dry and wet risers to automatic sprinkler systems. Whilst dry and wet risers are not usually for first-aid fire-fighting, they will help the fire brigade to tackle a fire quickly. The continued availability of these in existing buildings and their early commissioning in new buildings is therefore recommended. Similarly with sprinkler systems, it is worthwhile planning the work so that these are available for as much of the construction phase as possible.

Compartmentation

134 To stop a fire spreading, a building can be subdivided by fire-resisting walls and floors (ceilings). This is called compartmentation and a possible example of this was discussed in the protected stairway (see *Stairways*, paragraph 94). Compartmentation might also form a major part of the fire strategy for the completed building, especially for the larger and more complex structures. The early installation and completion of compartments

can also provide protection during the construction phase. It should be given priority when planning GFPs, but in practice there will be limits on how early compartmentation can be installed. Any openings need to be protected to an equivalent standard of fire resistance to the rest of the compartment. Work activities also need to be carefully monitored to ensure that any holes or gaps remaining after services are installed are correctly filled in.

135 Larger, more complex and prestige buildings may entail fire-safety engineering solutions, making use, for example, of smoke control systems. The installation of the complete fire-safety engineered package of safeguards is recommended to be completed as soon as possible. However, this cannot always be achieved and in the interim temporary compartmentation may be needed during the construction phase, eg of an atrium.

136 Temporary compartmentation providing a nominal period of 0.5 hour fire resistance may be achieved by a timber studding framework faced with 12.5 milli-metres thick plasterboard, skimmed with 5 millimetres of plaster to protect the joints. Alternatively, proprietary mineral fibre

Typical emergency lighting units designed to operate in the event of mains failure. Emergency lights can usefully incorporate fire safety signs

reinforced cement boards can be used. Typically, boards need to be fixed to both sides of the studding. However, where it is concluded that the compartmentation is required to contain a fire on one side only, boards may only be needed on that side. Take the advice of the supplier on the methods of fixing and finishing needed to achieve the period of fire resistance in such circumstances.

Emergency lighting

137   Normal lighting could well fail during a fire. If work carries on inside enclosed structures or at night, emergency escape lighting will normally be required to ensure that escape routes can be used safely. Escape lighting does not have to meet normal work standards but be adequate for people to use the route safely.

138   For work at night on outdoor or substantially open sites, spill lighting from adjacent sites or locations (eg, from street lighting) may be enough to enable escape.

139   Within buildings and enclosed structures, escape lighting (especially in escape routes) will generally be needed in the following circumstances:

(a)   underground or windowless accommodation;

(b)   stairs without natural, borrowed or spill lighting;

(c)   internal corridors without borrowed light, which are of sufficient length that the escape route would be unclear;

(d)   where work continues outside daylight hours.

140   In the event of failure of the primary lighting, the emergency escape lighting needs to come on immediately. It may be powered, eg by a battery or emergency generator supply. Lighting installed in compliance with BS EN 1838: 1999 is acceptable. If work is carried out in buildings in which such emergency lighting is already fitted, try to retain this for as long as possible. Similarly if it is to be installed in a new building, try to arrange that the emergency lighting is done as early as possible.

141   The use of way-finding methods, such as photo-luminescent signs and paints, to indicate key escape route features can be useful. For example, to emphasise changes of floor level, stairs and ladders, and obstructions such as pipes or features which extend into the escape route.

142   The correct operation of the escape lighting systems should be:

(a)   routinely checked and tested by a responsible person;

(b)   periodically serviced and any necessary rectification or repair carried out by a competent person having the appropriate level of training and experience;

(c)   the work should be carried out in accordance with the supplier's instructions or, where relevant, to the appropriate standard, for example BS EN 1838: 1999. Keep records of the work carried out.

143   Test escape lighting at a time of minimum risk, eg when the site is substantially unoccupied. Powered systems usually need to recharge, and photo-luminescent systems need to be reactivated after tests.

Emergency procedures

4

144 The previous section described physical GFP measures. This section describes the management procedures to make sure that the physical measures will work effectively if they are ever needed. The key element is an effective emergency plan. This guidance concentrates on fire. However, there may be other problems, such as flooding in excavations, tunnels, work near the sea or rivers, waterworks, etc, or risk from asphyxiation or toxic gases. These should be integrated with fire procedures. Plan emergency procedures before the work begins and put general precautions in place to support these from the start of the work.

145 On existing occupied sites, liaise and agree emergency procedures with the other occupiers. Ensure that the means are in place to let each other know straight away if an emergency does arise. If simultaneous evacuation is needed, make sure the escape routes are of sufficient capacity to achieve this.

146 Some emergencies may require total evacuation of the site, eg where it comprises a single multi-storey structure. Some emergencies may only require partial evacuation, eg where a series of separate structures are present on the site. Careful thought needs to be given to ensuring that the means provided are appropriate and capable of achieving the desired goal.

Developing an action plan for fire

147 All emergency plans need to be clear, unambiguous and known to all who are on the site. When developing plans consider the following aspects.

(a) Where will workers gather after evacuation from the site? (See *Assembly points*, paragraph 109.)

(b) Who will be in charge of the situation and what will be their role? What information and/or training will that person need to carry out those functions? Fire wardens may need to be appointed to assist the person in charge (see *Fire wardens*, paragraph 149).

(c) How will the people in charge communicate with each other?

(d) Checking that everyone has reached the assembly point, eg head counts or checking off against site security logs brought to the assembly point.

(e) Contacting the emergency services.

(f) Meeting the emergency services when they arrive and providing them with information. They will need to know of any particular risks, such as the location of LPG cylinders and the likely whereabouts of anyone unaccounted for who may still be on site.

148 The number of people involved in managing the emergency response should be kept to a necessary minimum. This will reduce the scope for confusion between different parties carrying out different tasks during the emergency. Nominate and train deputies to cover for key personnel when they are absent, eg for sickness or holidays.

Fire wardens

149 On larger sites the appointment of fire wardens, may be appropriate to:

(a) check that the site fire precaution rules are observed, and that the GFPs remain adequate, available and in good order;

(b) liaise with the fire brigade if there is a fire and provide information on access, people trapped and any special hazards, etc.

It is important that when such people are appointed, they are given the necessary authority to carry out their tasks.

Liaison with the fire services

150 In some cases it will be appropriate for those managing construction work to liaise with the local fire services before work starts. (Those holding fire certificates are also required to inform the fire authority of any material changes to the premises concerned under the Fire Precautions Act 1971.) Where there is liaison, it is important that fire services are kept informed of any changes affecting access and fire-fighting facilities as the work progresses.

151 Liaison with the fire services may be relevant, especially on large sites, or if any of the following apply:

(a) a substantial risk to the public, eg where fire in a large city centre site may result in the need for large-scale evacuation of heavily occupied neighbouring sites;

(b) where there are particular risks posed to fire-fighters, eg the presence of large numbers of gas cylinders or flammable liquids on site;

(c) where fire service access to the site may be difficult, for instance if access roads are narrow and congested or there is no access available to one side of a large site;

(d) where water supplies are limited or do not exist, eg a large factory development in a greenfield site;

(e) where work takes place above 18 metres (specialist access equipment may be required) and anywhere else where specialised rescue equipment may be needed, eg tunnels;

(f) where sleeping accommodation is provided for construction employees.

152 Liaison with the fire services may not mean all their problems can be solved, but it provides them with important information which they can use to plan their response, especially for higher-risk sites.

Monitoring GFPs and fire practices

153 It is important that escape routes are checked regularly. The frequency of this will depend on the complexity of the site and the rate of change. Usually at least a weekly check will be needed, and on larger and higher-risk sites a daily check of the main escape routes.

154 Fire alarm systems should be checked weekly, to ensure that they work and can be heard in real conditions. This should be at the same time each week, and people informed that the alarm at this time is a test. Keep simple records.

155 Fire drills, in which the entire workforce evacuates the site, are a useful means of checking that the GFP routines are effective. However, it is recognised these can often be impracticable, and because of the continually changing nature of sites and the workforce on them, of limited use. But as the risks of, and from, fire increase and the number of people on site rises, the need for at least one drill increases (often when the main structure of the building is complete) in order to check for problems, such as 'bottlenecks', etc.

156 In the absence of periodic fire drills, it is still important to check that those on site really do know what to do if there is a fire. Asking individual workers: 'What is the fire alarm?' and 'What would you do?', are a useful way of checking that the instruction and information has been adequate.

Fire instruction notices

157 Fire instruction notices should be permanently and prominently displayed on major escape routes, places where people meet, circulation spaces, etc. They should clearly outline:

(a) the action to be taken on discovering a fire including raising the alarm and first-aid fire-fighting;

(b) the action to be taken on hearing the fire alarm including evacuation, assembly and accounting for people.

158 On larger and higher-risk sites consider supplementing these notices with information specifically given to the individual, eg as a card with the pay packet or information during site induction procedures. Site visitors also need to be made aware of what to do if there is a fire.

PSA FIRE ORGANISATION

Address:
Fire Precautions Officer: .... Room .... Extn ....
Deputy: .... Room .... Extn ....

FIRE ACTION

RAISE THE ALARM

CALL FIRE BRIGADE

At Night

ON HEARING THE FIRE ALARM

Your Assembly Point is ....

Do Not Stop to Collect Personal Belongings

Attack Fire With Available Equipment if You Feel Safe to do so

Obey Instructions From Floor Wardens or Fire Brigade

Do Not Re-enter Building Until Told it is Safe

For guidance on completing this card please see Fire Precautions Guide – Leaflet 02 (1984 Edition). W2180 (Rev 1984)

Printed in the UK for HMSO Dd ACC475 9.91 C16 0652 4057

Typical fire notice format with space for entering clear and concise instructions on what to do if there is a fire

Information, instruction and training

159 The fire instruction notices are only intended to serve as a reminder. All people on site, even if they are there for just a few hours, should receive sufficient information to know what to do in the event of fire.

160 The minimum information which needs to be given, and should be given to people the first day they are on site, is:

(a) the location and use of the escape routes from their working area;

(b) the location and operation of the first warning system in their working area.

People will need to be updated on any changes.

161 People required to perform specific functions in the event of fire should be given the additional instruction and training needed for them to carry out their duties. For example:

(a) anyone expected to use fire-fighting equipment, including an extinguisher, should be given instruction and if necessary training on the correct selection and use of this. In particular, they need to know when to tackle a fire and when to leave it;

(b) equipment such as oxyacetylene equipment, bitumen boilers, etc, can turn small fires into very big ones if they are left on during a fire. Those in charge of such equipment should be instructed to turn them off, where this can be safely achieved without danger to themselves;

(c) fire wardens, where they are expected to liaise with the fire brigade, require information to do this role effectively. They need to be kept up to date with changes to the site, including those which might affect access for the fire brigade, the location and number of people on site, processes presenting a high fire risk and availability of water.

Temporary accommodation units

This timber hut can catch fire easily and would quickly fill the surrounding structure with smoke making escape more difficult

162 This section concerns temporary accommodation units (TAUs) such as offices and canteens occupied by people at work on construction sites. The standards described only apply to accommodation provided during the construction phase. **They are not requirements for completed buildings.**

163 TAUs can vary from very simple single site huts or caravans to complex composite units housing many staff.

164 TAUs are usually situated in the open air, but where they are located inside structures this gives rise to particularly acute risks, since smoke will accumulate very rapidly and escape routes become blocked very quickly. In addition, they can set the entire structure on fire, putting everyone on the site at risk.

165 Only use TAUs for their intended purpose. Offices in particular should not be used for storing materials, especially highly flammable ones such as paint.

166 In some cases, the Fire Certificates (Special Premises) Regulations 1976 apply to a temporary office, workshop or storage accommodation. If they do, the person in control of the TAU should apply for a certificate from the local office of the Health and Safety Executive. *Appendix 2* describes when an application should be made.

167 Preventing fire is the primary aim, but being able to deal with it is also important. In simple cases, such as a single site hut located on an open site, little beyond basic precautionary measures are appropriate such as:

(a) keeping a tidy office;

(b) providing a fire extinguisher;

(c) smoking rules;

(d) correct installation and careful use of heaters and cooking equipment (see *LPG*, paragraph 40);

(e) properly installed and maintained electrical services (see *Electrical installations*, paragraph 73).

More extensive precautions in the following paragraphs are required as TAUs and the associated fire risks increase in size and complexity.

Siting and fire integrity of TAUs

168 Ideally, TAUs should be located away from the building work (6 metres) In the open air. If TAUs have to be located closer, the risk of a TAU fire spreading can be reduced if either the TAU or the part of the building adjacent to it is fire resisting. If TAUs are sited inside buildings or structures, their fire resistance needs to be considered more carefully. The Loss Prevention Council Standard LPS 1195 sets out fire resistance criteria which are appropriate in these circumstances.

169 This standard applies specifically to temporary buildings and not parts of existing buildings, but the same standard may be useful in informing what requirements the latter should meet.

170 Where TAUs are vertically stacked the roof/floor assembly and the supporting members should be protected to achieve 0.5 hour fire resistance.

Means of escape

171 TAU complexes can be assembled in many different combinations. As they increase in size and complexity, particularly careful consideration needs to be given to ensuring that:
(a) there are at least two means of escape in different directions;
(b) if escape is possible in only one direction the escape route is adequately protected so that if it is ever needed it can be used;
(c) sufficient escape stairs are provided and protected.

Raising the alarm

172 All TAU complexes should be provided with a means of raising the alarm. The nature of it will vary, but the main requirement is for it to be audible throughout the complex.

173 An electrical break-glass system complying with BS 5839: Part 1, 1988 is likely to be needed where:
(a) more than 20 people are present at any one time;

(b) more than 10 people are present at any one time above the ground floor;
(c) the complex comprises three storeys or more than five rooms.

174 For fewer people and smaller complexes manually operated devices which are clearly audible to all those in the complex may be adequate, but self-contained electrically operated alarms comprising actuation switch and sounder are preferred.

175 Regularly test both manual and more sophisticated fire alarms to check that they work and can be heard in real conditions. Keep simple records.

176 For individual and pairs of non-compartmented TAUs a shout of 'fire' is adequate provided it can be heard in practical circumstances.

177 For TAUs within the building under construction, the TAU alarm system should be integrated with that for the rest of the building.

Fire-fighting equipment

178 Provide all TAUs, however simple, with some form of fire-fighting equipment and a sufficient number of hand-held extinguishers. The most typical fire risk in TAUs involves materials such as wood and paper. Water-based extinguishers should be provided for this.

179 Where large pieces of electrical equipment are used, eg computers or photocopiers, CO_2 extinguishers should be provided.

180 Provide TAUs where flammable liquids or similar materials are kept with dry powder extinguishers.

181 In kitchen and canteen areas where cooking oils are used, fire blankets should be provided.

Staff instruction and training

182 Emergency plans should take TAUs into account as well as the rest of the site.

Sleeping accommodation

183 Some projects may involve sleeping accommodation for construction workers. High standards of GFPs are required and there should be liaison with the fire service. Providing sleeping accommodation is a designated use under the Fire Precautions Act 1971 and a fire certificate from the local fire authority may be needed.

184 The detailed requirements will vary depending on the circumstances involved. The fundamental principles in this guidance for minimising the risk of fire occurring, and preparing for it if it does, apply to sleeping accommodation. Those principles need to be addressed in depth for sleeping accommodation. The details are beyond the scope of this guidance and specialist fire safety expertise will normally be required.

185 Workers should never be allowed to sleep on the working construction site itself.

186 Worker caravan parks are sometimes provided. Caravans are often highly combustible and fire can spread quickly between them if they are parked close together. Fire prevention and precautions need to be planned for caravan sleeping accommodation as much as any other, but particular attention should be given to:

(a) adequate space between vehicles - a minimum 6 metre separation is recommended;

(b) provision of adequate emergency alarm and fire-fighting equipment.

Appendices

Who enforces which legislation?

1 Because of the overlapping nature of construction-related and other fire-safety legislation, inspectors from three different agencies have different enforcement powers to deal with fire matters **during the course of construction work**. They are inspectors from:

(a) Health and Safety Executive;
(b) local authorities;
(c) the local fire authority.

2 The following flow chart indicates which inspector is the appropriate one for enforcement in which circumstance. Enquiries are best directed towards the agency that has the enforcement power for the particular issue concerned.

3 Even if inspectors do not have formal enforcement powers for the situation concerned they may still visit construction sites for other reasons. They may address fire matters, but if they do not have the appropriate enforcement powers they can refer the matter to the appropriate authority if enforcement action seems appropriate.

4 The flow chart uses abbreviations as follows:

HSW Health and Safety at Work etc Act 1974;

CHSW Construction (Health, Safety and Welfare) Regulations 1996. Regulation 18 is concerned with preventing fire occurring and regulations 19-21 are concerned with being able to deal with it if it happens;

HFL Highly Flammable Liquids and Liquefied Petroleum Gases Regulations 1972;

CDM Construction (Design and Management) Regulations 1994;

MHSW Management of Health and Safety at Work Regulations 1999;

FCSP Fire Certificate (Special Premises) Regulations 1976;

LA Local authority;

HSE Health and Safety Executive;

FA Fire authority.

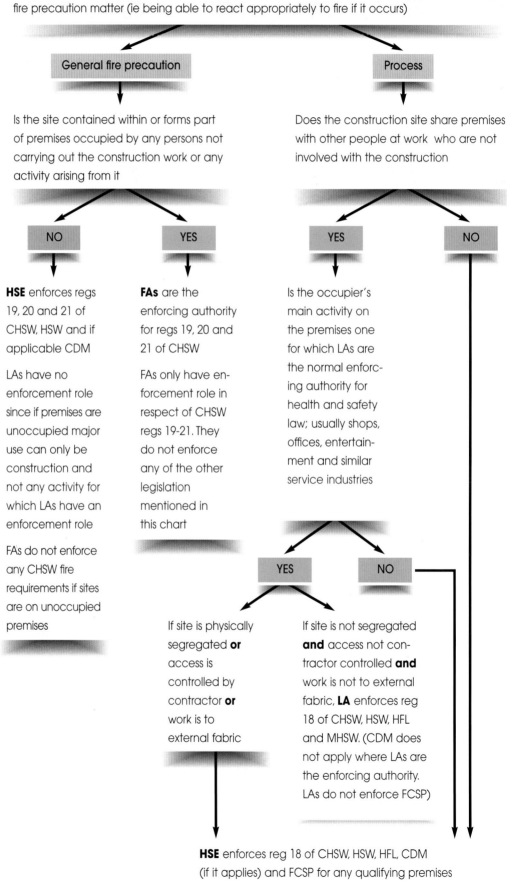

Is the fire problem a process matter (ie preventing fire occurring in the first place) or is it a general fire precaution matter (ie being able to react appropriately to fire if it occurs)

General fire precaution

Process

Is the site contained within or forms part of premises occupied by any persons not carrying out the construction work or any activity arising from it

Does the construction site share premises with other people at work who are not involved with the construction

NO

YES

YES

NO

HSE enforces regs 19, 20 and 21 of CHSW, HSW and if applicable CDM

LAs have no enforcement role since if premises are unoccupied major use can only be construction and not any activity for which LAs have an enforcement role

FAs do not enforce any CHSW fire requirements if sites are on unoccupied premises

FAs are the enforcing authority for regs 19, 20 and 21 of CHSW

FAs only have enforcement role in respect of CHSW regs 19-21. They do not enforce any of the other legislation mentioned in this chart

Is the occupier's main activity on the premises one for which LAs are the normal enforcing authority for health and safety law; usually shops, offices, entertainment and similar service industries

YES

NO

If site is physically segregated **or** access is controlled by contractor **or** work is to external fabric

If site is not segregated **and** access not contractor controlled **and** work is not to external fabric, **LA** enforces reg 18 of CHSW, HSW, HFL and MHSW. (CDM does not apply where LAs are the enforcing authority. LAs do not enforce FCSP)

HSE enforces reg 18 of CHSW, HSW, HFL, CDM (if it applies) and FCSP for any qualifying premises such as site offices

The Fire Certificates (Special Premises) Regulations 1976: Where and when they apply

1 A fire certificate is needed for buildings or any part of a building which is:

(a) constructed for temporary occupation for construction purposes; or

(b) already in existence when the construction work starts; and

(c) used for processes or work 'ancillary' to construction.

2 It is not just proprietary 'bolt together' accommodation units that are included. If rooms in existing buildings are used for similar purposes they can also require certificates.

3 To require a certificate the accommodation has to be used for ancillary purposes. Not all temporary accommodation is ancillary to construction work. To be ancillary it has to be something that is associated with the actual construction process. Site offices are ancillary because administration is needed for efficient organisation of construction work. They are the most common premises for which certificates are required. Canteens are not ancillary because comfortable eating facilities are not necessary in the same way.

4 Even if (a)-(c) above are satisfied, a fire certificate is not required if **all** the following conditions are satisfied:

(a) no more than 20 people are employed at any one time in the accommodation;

(b) no more than 10 people are employed at any one time elsewhere than on the ground floor;

(c) no explosive or highly flammable materials are stored or used in or under the building;

(d) adequate means of escape are provided;

(e) adequate fire-fighting facilities are provided;

(f) exit doors can be opened from the inside when anyone is in the building;

(g) stairway and corridor doors open outwards;

(h) escape doors, windows or other exits are well-indicated;

(i) room contents are arranged to allow free passage if there is a fire.

5 If a certificate is required the 'responsible person' has to apply to HSE for one. The responsible person means the person who has control of the accommodation concerned. In practice this will most often be the principal contractor (or the main contractor where CDM does not apply)

How to stop fire occurring

Clients

Provide information to the planning supervisor on:

- site rules on fire safety standards at occupied premises;
- location of buried services;
- previous contents of tanks;
- previous uses of site and flammable materials likely to be present as a result;
- special precautions required for fire-sensitive activities nearby, eg chemical processing;
- limits on site storage areas;
- arrangements for, or limitations on, rubbish disposal.

Appoint competent and adequately resourced planning supervisors and principal contractors. Ask questions where fire is an important issue, for instance construction work at a fuel storage depot or partial refurbishment of a heavily occupied city centre office block. Ask about:

- previous experience of similar work;
- internal arrangements already existing to address fire issues;
- how candidates suggest dealing with the particular project's fire problems.

Where your activities overlap with those of a contractor, you might need to become involved in the operational management of site activities. However, the principal contractor has the main responsibility for co-ordinating site safety in these circumstances.

Designers

Consider your proposals in terms of the amount of flammable materials that are specified. If they are used only in small amounts the risk may be insignificant, but as the amount and variety of potentially flammable substances involved in a project increases, your role in their selection becomes increasingly important in controlling workplace risks.

You need to know if the materials you are specifying are flammable or not, and if they are, to what extent. If you don't know, find out from manufac-turers or suppliers. If less flammable alternatives are available, specify them unless there is a particular design reason why a more flammable one has to be used instead. Particular attention needs to be paid to the selection of:

- paints;
- solvents;
- adhesives.

Consider if the use of such substances is really necessary. For instance, do you need to paint the wall of an underground car park at all?

The sequence of construction may have implications for fire loads. For example, if vulnerable internal fittings are designed for installation last, the need to protect them with potentially flammable coverings will be reduced.

Provide relevant health and safety information with your design for those who may need it during subsequent construction work. This could include:

- highlighting where significant amounts of flammable materials are specified;
- information on intended installation sequences.

Planning supervisors

Pre-tender stage health and safety plans may need to consider site-wide fire issues and provide relevant information on fire risks, eg:

- location and nature of flammable substances on site;
- location of gas services;
- nature of nearby activities, especially if they are sensitive to site-generated fire risks or pose fire risk to the construction work;
- details of any likely continued occupation of the site (especially in office or residential projects);
- details of any intended construction processes or methods which lead to high fire risk.

It may also be possible and appropriate at the pre-tender stage to set out generally applicable site standards. This is more likely where premises are shared with occupiers and their needs have to be considered in the site arrangements. For example, there may be constraints arising from the occupiers needs on:

- rubbish removal and clearance;
- nature and location of flammables storage.

This does not detract from the principal contractor's duty to develop the subsequent construction phase plan, but it is legitimate for the planning supervisor to describe the general limitations within which the construction phase plan has to be drawn up.

Principal contractors

Draw up the construction phase health and safety plan. This should describe the day-to-day standards to be observed on site. Site rules within the plan can be a particularly important part of controlling the accumulation of flammable materials. Site rules can include standards to be followed on:

- frequency of rubbish clearance by contractors;
- location and nature of rubbish storage facilities to be provided;
- frequency of emptying communal skips;
- bringing flammable substances onto site;
- storage arrangements for any flammables brought onto site.

Make sure that contractors' and individuals' responsibilities in implementing fire precautions are clearly identified.

Make sure site workers are familiar with site rules and procedures. Prominent display of notices and/or inclusion of rules with pay packet slips are effective means. On larger sites involving higher risks and large numbers of contractors, site induction training may be more appropriate.

Whenever necessary give the construc-tion phase health and safety plan, and rules contained in it, to subcontractors during the tendering process. Usually it is simpler for contractors to build decided fire safety standards into their tender proposals at this stage, than later on when it becomes more difficult to amend developed proposals.

Make sure parties are complying with the plan. Mere drafting of site rules in themselves will not ensure adequate standards are achieved on site. Arrange for positive inspection of fire safety standards. You can either do this yourself or delegate monitoring responsibilities to other parties.

Inspection regimes may vary from site to site. Where fire risks are low such as during the frame erection stage of a steel frame building, inspection for fire matters will be a low priority compared to potential falls during steel erection. However, fire safety will, for example, require much closer monitoring during the fit-out stage of an office refurbishment contract.

If poor fire safety standards or non-compliance with site rules are found during inspection, you will need to resolve such matters. Where risks are high a formal and systematic approach for resolving shortcomings may be needed to ensure that action is taken. This is especially significant where many different contractors are present on the same site.

Contractors

Both you and your employees need to comply with site rules. Either the employing contractor or the principal contractor should be able to provide appropriate information. It will often be more convenient for the principal contractor to do this, eg through site induction procedures, but this does not alter your duty to ensure your own employees are adequately informed. There should be clear understanding between principal contractors and contractors on how the information is to be provided and by whom.

Provide the principal contractor with relevant information on fire safety matters. In particular, inform principal contractors where there are difficulties in complying with the health and safety plan or where fire safety issues are discovered which are not addressed by the existing plan. For example, inform principal contractors if:

- you need to bring significant amounts of flammable materials onto site not envisaged by the health and safety plan;
- rubbish skips are not being emptied;
- flammable material is discovered during work, eg groundworkers discover drums of buried waste or unforeseen gas services during excavations.

Reducing ignition sources

Clients

Ignition sources on site during the construction phase are largely outside your control, so usually you will not have much relevant or useful additional information to provide to planning supervisors.

In some cases you may wish to specify operational constraints, to take into account the risks to your own employees who may be affected by the construction work, especially if the work is in high-risk areas such as in a chemical plant.

Designers

Ignition sources are usually on site more as a result of the way contractors carry out their work rather than the designs that they are attempting to construct. However, you can reduce the need for hot work in your designs, for example:

- Can steel components be fabricated off site rather than being welded on site?
- Can steel sections be bolted rather than welded together?
- Can you specify push or thread fit plumbing connections rather than brazed jointing?

Planning supervisors

Successful control of ignition sources is largely dependent on detailed day-to-day site control, but some site-wide constraints may be appropriate for inclusion in the pre-tender health and safety plan, especially where such matters arise from constraints placed by the client, for example:

- the need for hot work permit-to-work systems for certain high-risk circumstances.

Principal contractors

The construction phase health and safety plan and site rules arising from it are a primary means of managing ignition risks. This is especially significant in situations where there are many trades on site requiring tight management control to ensure that they all comply with appropriate standards. The detail required in the plan will depend on the level and extent of risks on the individual site concerned. Construction phase plans can usefully consider the following.

- Permit-to-work systems - are they necessary? If they are:
  - Who will administer and control their implementation?
  - What sort of work will they apply to?
  - Where on the site will they apply?
- Details of any smoking policy. If designated smoking areas are to be provided where will they be?
- Scrutiny of proposals for high-risk work in detail, eg tank demolition. Subsequent agreement with the contractor concerned, of detailed safety method statement and confirmation of clear and specific rules relating to the work.
- Specification of any banned or restricted equipment or activities, for example:
  - unauthorised additions to electrical system;
  - use of blowlamps;
  - possession of lighters;
  - lighting of fires.
- Nomination of specified electrical contractor and clarification of their role.
- Details of site security arrangements and the allocation of clear authority to security staff to carry out their work.

You may need to amend site rules as circumstances change during construction.

Make sure that there is active monitoring for compliance with site rules. Allocate clear responsibilities for this and ensure that on-site managers are provided with the necessary authority to demand that shortcomings are rectified. You may wish to specify disciplinary action to deal with persistent breaches of site rules.

The construction phase plan and any site rules should be disseminated to contractors and the workforce.

Contractors

Consider information and standards provided in your tendering proposals.

Make sure that you and any of your employees are familiar with site rules and comply with them.

If you are carrying out work involving particular ignition risks such as welding or plumbing, make sure your employees are familiar with the risks involved and competent to deal with fire if it breaks out. For instance, welders and plumbers should be familiar with the nature of permit-to-work systems, and the basic precautions required. You may need to co-operate with principal contractors in achieving this by providing information and training at sites.

Both you and your employees should inform the principal contractor of any relevant matters which arise during the work. For example:

- poor or damaged electrical installations or equipment;
- occurrence of any minor fires;
- difficulties met in complying with site rules, for instance if a need to use blowlamps develops but the site rules ban their use.

General fire precautions

Clients

Providing general fire precautions on site is often outside your control so you will have little role in providing them.

If during the construction phase existing precautions installed in your building need to be maintained, you should provide the planning supervisor with relevant information. This might include:

- location of dry and wet risers;
- installation diagrams of the fire alarm system;
- operational status of equipment, eg are the sprinklers still connected?
- existing means of escape provision.

Planning supervisors

General fire precautions are a site-wide issue, so you need to address them in the pre-tender stage health and safety plan. Information on design conclusions relevant to construction phase fire safety should be included in the pre-tender health and safety plan. Principal contractors need this information to arrange for appropriate construction sequences so that, for example, protected stairways are installed at an early stage.

Designers

You will have little influence on the provision of temporary precautions provided solely during the construction phase, such as hand-held fire extinguishers. You have more potential in providing design features to improve general fire precaution standards during construction. The following matters can usually be considered. Many of them will be required anyway as part of the specification for the completed building. It should often be straightforward providing them for the benefit of construction workers as well as the final occupants.

- Arrange for wet and dry risers to be installed early in the construction sequence. This is important in high-rise projects.
- Arrange for compartmentation to be introduced at as early a stage as possible. This may not always be easy to achieve but can substantially reduce the spread of fire and smoke where it is feasible and should be considered in higher-risk projects.
- Arrange for fire doors to be installed at an early stage, especially in protected stairway escape routes. Temporary doors can be specified during the construction phase if necessary to avoid damage to the final items.
- Internal stairways are usually a fundamental part of the design and can generally be installed at an early stage to provide protected means of escape. They also have the operational benefit of easing movement about the site.
- Consider installing permanent alarm systems at the start of the fit-out stage or before.

The above list contains some basic construction phasing issues. For instance, installation of primary stairways is dependent on and affects other design features. It is therefore important that you liaise with other designers and members of the project team on such matters.

Principal contractors

You need to address general fire precautions in the construction phase health and safety plan. Underlying design assumptions (such as phasing of stairway installation) should already have been made clear and indicated to you in the pre-tender health and safety plan from the planning supervisor. You will need to ensure that those criteria are reflected in construction sequences and methods. Provide relevant information to the contractors concerned with those parts of the project. Both you and the contractor should be clear about who is doing what and when so that you can comply with design decisions.

The construction phase plan also needs to address detailed operational matters as well as the implementation of design criteria. Items could include:

- nature, amount and location of fire points;
- arrangements for inspecting and maintaining fire-fighting equipment;
- clarification of the arrangements for alarm and checking that it is effective;
- any arrangements for provision of emergency power and lighting. What is to be provided and by whom?
- work on protected means of escape requiring openings to be made in them. Can this be done at weekends or during slack times so that the minimum number of people are at risk if a fire occurs when the fire resistance of the escape route is compromised?
- clarification of the role of scaffolding as a means of escape;
- specific site rules, eg
  - keep means of escape clear;
  - no horseplay with extinguishers;
  - inform management if extinguishers are used.

Make sure parties follow the construction phase plan. Take positive action if they are not doing so.

Contractors

Make sure that you and your employees comply with site rules and other elements of the construction phase plan. Are you and your workers aware of relevant parts of the plan? In practice this may often be achieved through the principal contractor informing your employees direct, but you should not merely assume this will happen. If you think that site induction training will be provided, for example, check that this is the case.

Inform the principal contractor of any problems in complying with the plan, non-compliance with it or shortcomings noted in it. It is especially important that anyone installing design features such as stairways, who anticipates or finds problems in complying with the standards or times specified in the plan, should tell the principal contractor.

Emergency procedures

Clients

If you share occupied premises with construction workers, provide information on existing emergency arrangements to the planning supervisor. This could include information on the following:

- when you will have fire drills;
- limitations on the location of assembly points;
- existing arrangements with local fire services.

If there is a need for the occupier and construction emergency arrangements to be integrated, you should co-operate with the planning supervisor and the principal contractor to achieve this.

Designers

Fire brigade access may be easy once the building is finished, but you should consider the building footprint in relation to the access that will be available during construction, eg when roads will not be completed and the site will be obstructed by materials, plant, site huts, etc. In higher-risk projects such as tall structures with large numbers of contractors at work, you should consider this in more depth.

Principal contractors

You should devise an adequately detailed emergency plan (taking into account the risks involved) and ensure it is incorporated in the construction phase health and safety plan. The following elements should always be included:

- location of assembly points;
- instructions on what to do in the event of fire;
- identification of who is in charge if there is a fire and a description of their role.

In low-risk situations the contents of emergency plans may be very simple indeed. Where, in the event of a fire, higher risks are involved, the following items may also need to be included in construction phase plans:

- regular fire drills;
- special arrangements for evacuation from high-risk areas, eg the LPG store;
- appointment of specialist fire wardens;
- regular liaison with local fire services;
- liaison with occupiers of shared premises;
- fire-fighting training for those carrying out high-risk work.

If the nature of the site changes significantly, the emergency arrangements will need to be revised accordingly. For example, what is required during frame erection will be much less and very different from what is needed during the fit-out stage.

Make sure that everyone on the site is familiar with the emergency arrangements.

Planning supervisors

Pre-tender stage health and safety plans should include information available that would influence the development of the construction phase plan by the principal contractor, for example:

- available access for fire services;
- available areas for assembly points;
- existing emergency arrangements on occupied sites.

The generation of emergency plans for the construction phase is the role of the principal contractor, so you will not normally be involved in this.

Contractors

Both you and your staff need to be familiar with the emergency arrangements. In practice this will often be achieved by the principal contractor providing information. You should not merely assume that this will happen and should clarify with the principal contractor how the information is to be provided. This will normally be achieved during the tendering process.

Make sure that you and your employees co-operate with the principal contractor, eg attending induction training and participating in fire drills where required to do so.

Report any shortcomings to principal contractors, eg if any employees have not attended site induction training.

Temporary accommodation units

Clients

If you need to place restrictions on the siting of TAUs, tell the planning supervisor and relevant designers at an early stage.

If you provide site accommodation, co-operate with the principal contractor so that the appropriate standards are met, especially if the accommodation is within the building or structure being worked on.

Designers

In most cases you will be concerned with the finished building rather than the temporary accommodation during the construction phase. Even if you have no direct involvement with the design of TAUs, you should allow space for them when considering the general layout of the structure. Ideally designs should allow space for TAUs to be sited outside the structure. If this is not possible, consider suitable locations for internal accommodation and inform the planning supervisor of your conclusions.

Planning supervisors

Consider temporary accommodation needs in your pre-tender stage health and safety plans. You should not usually be concerned with the practical details of operational TAU requirements. However, pre-tender stage plans should normally contain information on:
- any limitations on where TAUs can be sited;
- any information from designers on TAU location.

Principal contractors

The construction phase health and safety plan should set out the arrangements for TAU provision. TAU arrangements are one of the first elements to be decided in the construction phase plan, since they are provided right from the start of construction.

Where large or higher-risk TAUs are involved, construction phase health and safety plans should normally consider:
- where the accommodation will be sited;
- the standards it needs to meet;
- necessary fire precautions;
- who is responsible for providing satisfactory accommodation (eg principal contractor or nominated contractor).

Where you are the 'responsible person', you should apply to HSE for a fire certificate if there is TAU provision covered by the Fire Certificates (Special Premises) Regulations.

Tell contractors about any site rules concerning TAU fire precautions. Contractors will especially need to know any limits or controls on storing materials inside TAUs to plan their work. Inform contractors of these matters at an early stage, preferably during the tendering process.

Contractors

Make sure that you and your employees know and comply with site rules and standards concerning TAUs. In practice this may be achieved by instructions and information provided direct by the principal contractor, but you should not merely assume this will happen. If there is any doubt, liaise with the principal contractor to check that the necessary information or instruction has been provided.

Provide principal contractors with any relevant information. This could include information on:
- damage to the fire-resistant integrity of accommodation;
- non-compliance with site rules;
- a need for additional TAU material storage space;
- damage to fire alarms or fire-fighting equipment.

If you have specific responsibilities for providing TAUs, you should provide them in accordance with both the principles in this guidance and requirements in the construction phase plan.

Sleeping accommodation

Clients

Contractors may need to provide sleeping accommodation for construction workers. If so, let the planning supervisor know of any restrictions on where caravans or other sleeping accommodation can and cannot be sited.

Designers

If you are involved in the specification of cabins or sleeping accommodation for construction workers you will need to make sure that your proposals meet high fire safety standards. More detailed advice is available from fire prevention officers.

Planning supervisors

Provide principal contractors with information in the pre-tender health and safety plan on where sleeping accommodation can be sited and any design criteria it should meet.

Principal contractors

Specify the detailed requirements for sleeping accommodation in the construction phase plan. If you are not sure what the standards should be, get specialist advice. The local fire prevention officer can help.

- Monitor compliance with those requirements.
- Make sure that the contractors know what the requirements are before their employees arrive on site, and that employees know them when they arrive. This could be in the form of 'site' rules for the sleeping accommodation.
- Check with the local fire authority on the need for a fire certificate under the Fire Precautions Act 1971.

Contractors

Make sure that sleeping arrangements for your employees are satisfactorily resolved with the principal contractor before your employees arrive on site.

References and further reading

Relevant legislation

Construction (Health, Safety and Welfare) Regulations 1996: SI 1996/1592

Construction (Design and Management) Regulations 1994: SI 1994/3140

Fire Certificates (Special Premises) Regulations 1976: SI 1976/2003

Highly Flammable Liquids and Liquefied Petroleum Gases Regulations 1972: SI 1972/917

Management of Health and Safety at Work Regulations 1999: SI 1999/3242

Workplace (Health, Safety and Welfare) Regulations 1992: SI 1992/3004

Fire Precautions Act 1971: ISBN 0 11 805139 3

Fire Precautions (Workplace) Regulations 1997: SI 1997/1840, as amended by the Fire Precautions (Workplace)(Amendment) Regulations 1999, SI 1999/1877

HSE guidance (priced)

A guide to managing health and safety in construction (Practical Guidance on the Construction (Design and Management) Regulations) HSE Books 1995 ISBN 0 7176 0755 0

The cleaning and gas freeing of tanks containing flammable residues CS15 HSE Books 1985 ISBN 0 11 883518 1

Health and safety in demolition work Part 3: Techniques GS29/3 HSE Books 1984 ISBN 0 11 883609 9

The storage of flammable liquids in containers HSG51 HSE Books 1990 ISBN 0 7176 0481 0

The safe use and handling of flammable liquids HSG140 HSE Books 1996 ISBN 0 7176 0967 7

Electrical safety on construction sites HSG141 HSE Books 1995 ISBN 0 7176 1000 4

Health and safety in construction HSG150 HSE Books 1996 ISBN 0 7176 1143 4

The safe use of compressed gases in welding, flame cutting and allied processes HSG139 HSE Books 1997 ISBN 0 7176 0680 5

Home Office/Health and Safety Executive *Fire safety - an employer's guide* Stationery Office 1999 ISBN 0 11 341229 0

Approved codes of practice

Managing construction for health and safety Construction (Design and Management) Regulations 1994 Approved Code of Practice L54 HSE Books 1995 ISBN 0 7176 0792 5

Safety signs and signals: Guidance on regulations The Health and Safety (Safety Signs and Signals) Regulations 1996 L64 HSE Books 1996 ISBN 0 7176 0870 0

HSE guidance (free)

Signpost to safety signs regulations INDG184 HSE Books 1996. (Also available in priced packs, ISBN 0 7176 1139 6)

A guide to the Construction (Health, Safety and Welfare) Regulations 1996 INDG220 HSE Books 1996. (Also available in priced packs, ISBN 0 7176 1161 2)

Safe working with flammable substances INDG227 HSE Books 1996. (Also available in priced packs, ISBN 0 7176 1154 X)

Construction fire safety CISS1 HSE Books 1997

Relevant standards

There are a large number of standards which are principally concerned with the fire safety standards of completed buildings. They may be relevant to fire safety during construction work as well. The extent of their individual relevance depends on the nature and circumstances of the individual construction work concerned.

BS 476: Part 22,1987 *Fire tests on building materials and structures. Methods for determination of the fire resistance of non-loadbearing elements of construction.*

BS 1703: 1977 *Specification for refuse chutes and hoppers.*

BS 3212: 1991 *Specifications for flexible rubber tubing, rubber hosing and rubber hose assemblies for use in LPG vapour phase and LPG oblique air installations.*

BS 4363: 1991 *Distribution assemblies for electrical supplies for construction and building sites*

BS 5306: Part 1,1976 *Fire extinguishing installations and equipment on premises. Hydrant systems, hose reels and foam inlets*

BS 5306: Part 3, 2000 *Fire extinguishing installations and equipment on premises, Part 3 - Maintenance of portable fire extinguishers. Code of practice*

BS 5345: Part 2,1989 *Classification of hazardous areas*

BS 5423: 1987 (amended 1995) *Specification for portable fire extinguishers*

BS 5440: Part 1, 2000 *Installation and maintenance of flues and ventilation for gas appliances of rated input not exceeding 70 kW net, Part 1 - Specification for installation of flues*

BS 5440: Part 2, 2000 *Installation and maintenance of flues and ventilation for gas appliances of rated input not exceeding 70 kW net, Part 2 - Specification for installation of ventilation for gas appliances*

BS 5482: Part 2,1988 (amended 1997) *Domestic butane and propane gas burning installations. Installations in caravans and non permanent dwellings*

BS 5499: Part 1,1990 (amended 1993) *Fire safety signs, notices and graphic symbols. Fire safety signs*

BS 5588: *Fire precautions in the design, construction and use of buildings*

Part 0,1996 *Guide to fire safety codes of practice for particular premises*

Part 1,1990 *Code of practice for residential buildings*

Part 2,1985 *Code of practice for shops*

Part 3,1983 *Code of practice for office buildings*

Part 4,1978 *Code of practice for smoke control in protected escape routes using pressurization*

Part 5,1991 Code of practice for firefighting stairs and lifts

Part 6,1991 *Code of practice for places of assembly*

Part 9,1989 *Code of practice for ventilation and air conditioning ductwork*

Part 10,1991 *Code of practice for shopping complexes*

Part 11, 1997 *Code of practice for shops, offices, industrial, storage and other similar buildings*

BS 5839: Part 1,1988 (amended1996) *Fire detection and alarm systems for buildings. Code of practice for system design, installation and servicing*

BS 6187: 2000 *Code of practice for demolition*

BS 7261: 1990 *Safety of small non domestic flueless space heaters burning 3rd family gases*

BS 7375: 1996 *Code of practice for distribution of electricity on construction and building sites*

BS 7671: 1992 *Requirements for electrical installations and IEE regulations*

BS 8214: 1990 (amended 1992) *Code of practice for fire door assemblies with non-metallic leaves*

BS EN 3: 1996 *Portable fire extinguishers*

BS EN 521: 1998 *Specification for dedicated LPG appliances - Portable vapour pressure LPG appliances*

BS EN 559: 1994 *Gas welding equipment. Rubber hoses for welding, cutting and allied processes*

BS EN 585: 1995 *Gas welding equipment. Pressure regulators for gas cylinders used in welding, cutting and allied processes up to 200 bar*

BS EN 730: 1995 *Gas welding equipment. Equipment used in gas welding, cutting and allied processes, safety devices for fuel gases and oxygen or compressed air. General specifications, requirements and tests*

BS EN 1125: 1997 *Building hardware. Panic exit devices operated by a horizontal bar. Requirements and test methods*

BS EN 1596: 1998 *Specification for dedicated LPG appliances - Mobile and portable non-domestic forced convection direct fired air heaters*

BS EN 1838: 1999, BS 5266-7: 1999 *Lighting applications. Emergency lighting*

BS EN ISO 2503: 1998 *Gas welding equipment. Pressure regulators for gas cylinders used in welding, cutting and allied processes up to 300 bar*

BS EN 60309-1: 1999, IEC 60309-1: 1999 *Plugs, socket-outlets and couplers for industrial purposes. General requirements*

BS EN 60439-4: 1991 *Particular requirements for assemblies for construction sites*

Loss Prevention Council: Loss Prevention Standard 1195, Issue 3,1994 *Specification for testing of temporary buildings for use on construction sites*

Loss Prevention Council: Loss Prevention Standard 1207, Issue 1,1994 *Fire requirements for protective covering materials*

Loss Prevention Council: Loss Prevention Standard 1215 1996 *Flammable requirements for scaffold cladding materials*

Further reading

Fire Protection Association/Construction Confederation *Fire prevention on construction sites: The joint code of practice on the protection from fire of construction sites and buildings undergoing renovation* 5th edition Construction Confederation 2000 ISBN 0 9021 6739 1

British Compressed Gases Association *The safe use of oxy-fuel gas equipment (individual, portable or mobile cylinder supply)* Code of Practice No 7 1994

LP Gas Association Code of Practice 4 *Safe and satisfactory operation of propane-fired thermoplastic and bitumen boilers, mastic asphalt cauldrons/mixer, hand tools and similar equipment* 1998

LP Gas Association Code of Practice 7 *Storage of full and empty LPG cylinders and cartridges* 1998

LP Gas Association Code of Practice 24 Part 5 *The storage and use of LPG on construction sites* 2000

The future availability and accuracy of the references listed in this publication cannot be guaranteed

Printed and published by the Health and Safety Executive   C50   09/01